About the Author

Helen Germanos is a homeopath, Reiki practitioner and holds a degree in psychology. In 2012 she collapsed with Chronic Fatigue Syndrome and lay paralyzed in bed for just over nine months. Helen managed to recover from CFS using her skills to help herself and looking to others for help. As she began to recover she read through as much of the research and theories on CFS as she could find.

In the process she finally began to gain some understanding of what this illness is and how it actually affects people in a variety of different ways. During this time she also read information on body/mind research in an effort to try and pinpoint the underlying cause for developing this illness, and by understanding this, to ensure it did not happen again.

In April 2013 she read a research study, published in the US journal Psychophysiology from 1995, entitled 'Orienting in a defensive world: Mammalian modifications of our evolutionary heritage. A 'Polyvagal Theory' by Stephen Porges. It was this study that eventually led Helen to a complete understanding of how and why this illness develops and helped her in the final stages of her recovery back to full health. Helen quickly realized that it was from this moment of understanding that she was able to take her life and health back into her own hands. For this reason she decided to write this book, to share this knowledge with other sufferers and their carers in the hope that they too may benefit.

SILENT PAIN

HOW STRESS AND TRAUMA MAY LEAD
TO CHRONIC FATIGUE SYNDROME

A JOURNEY OF DISCOVERY AND TRANSFORMATION

HELEN GERMANOS

Matador
9 Priory Business Park
Kibworth Beauchamp
Leicestershire LE8 0RX, UK
Tel: (+44) 116 279 2299
Fax: (+44) 116 279 2277
Email: books@troubador.co.uk
Web: www.troubador.co.uk/matador

ISBN 978-1784621-438

Book edited by Bryony Weaver
Cover artwork by Marina Koufidaki: www.marinakoufidaki.gr

British Library Cataloguing in Publication Data.
A catalogue record for this book is available from the British Library.

Printed and bound in the UK by TJ International, Padstow, Cornwall
Typeset in 11pt Bembo by Troubador Publishing Ltd, Leicester, UK

Matador is an imprint of Troubador Publishing Ltd

It takes two to speak the truth —
one to speak and another to hear

— THOREAU

Chronic Fatigue Syndrome (CFS) is also known as Myalgic Encephalomyelitis (ME). In this book I will simply refer to this illness as CFS.

CONTENTS

Biographies

Colin Griffith MCH, HMA is a highly respected and effective practitioner of homeopathy. He studied at the College of Homeopathy and, instead of writing a thesis, set up a supervised drop-in clinic that continued for 11 years and became a teaching clinic where students under his supervision set up their own tables. He has always preferred to work in a multi-disciplinary practice where other complementary therapies are offered: cranial osteopathy, reflexology, counselling etc. He is a founder member of the Guild of Homeopaths and lectures regularly at the Centre for Homeopathic Education, Regent's College, London, and has lectured in America, Canada, Japan and Greece. He is the author of the highly regarded The Companion to Homeopathy, The Practical Handbook of Homeopathy, and The New Materia Medica, Volume I and II.

Susannah Burton is a Biodynamic Craniosacral Therapist, working in London. She is a graduate of the Craniosacral Therapy Educational Trust and has since been a tutor on their practitioner trainings. She is extremely committed and inspired by Craniosacral Therapy and through her continuing professional development has been awarded an Advanced Biodynamic Diploma by the International Affiliation of Biodynamic Trainings. She is also an active member of the Craniosacral Therapy Association. "I am extremely passionate about Craniosacral Therapy and continuously inspired by it, and have been lucky enough to meet and work with wonderful colleagues and clients, all of whom have contributed to my learning in so many ways. I have a particular interest in working with people with chronic and life-threatening illnesses, and am constantly amazed, and humbled, by how health can be found even in the presence of disease."

Amanda McGregor is a Creative Development Therapist working with the spirit of creation as a psychic healer, visionary, consultant and artist. Facilitating the spirit of creation to flow through her in healing, vision, collective consciousness and art, Amanda helps those who are in need, or who want to develop, by empowering them in limitless possibilities of the potential that they may embrace. A consultation with Amanda is an enlightening experience. Amanda works sensitively and purposefully, she psychically tunes in to your body's energy field and the universal body of consciousness, to bring forward visions and solutions, to change personal energy patterns and to bring stability and consistency to all aspects of your life.

Foreword

Much is spoken about Chronic Fatigue Syndrome these days and many more suffer from it than are diagnosed. Odd, then, that it is not a well understood condition, perhaps least of all by many in the orthodox medical field. One reason for this lack of understanding is that it is a syndrome rather than a disease; syndromes are far harder to pin down as they are a complex of a wide variety of symptoms which vary in number, intensity and influence on the body in each individual. Chronic Fatigue Syndrome (CFS) is hard to quantify or qualify and does not fit easily into the medical textbook; not least as there are no official treatments or drug regimes. Modern medicine has not caught up with the ills of mankind!

Good news indeed that Helen has written the story of her life with CFS: the blow-by-blow account of succumbing, suffering, searching for the path towards healing of this debilitating unwellness. She writes from the heart, the only place from which understanding might ever come when the origins are to be found not simply in the physical body but also in the subtle bodies of emotion and spirit.

Helen's text is simple, undogmatic, unpretentious and positive in tone. Those with CFS or practitioners who are asked to treat patients suffering with it will find ample food for thought and much inspiration. She is clear that recognition and understanding of the condition is the first step. She tells us that, as with all chronic ill health, true healing can only come from within; true cure can never be applied from outside the body. She is open-minded in her appraisal of those disciplines that offer support and healing; her intention is to suggest that sufferers should seek their own individual routes to health, not simply through choosing a therapy such as homoeopathy (her own practice) but other supportive measures as well… including, when appropriate, orthodox medical means.

Helen's success in overcoming this chronic life-blight is inspiring and, for those ready to take up the life-challenge it presents, her solutions to her own condition should act as a map of options. For practitioners of alternative therapies this slim volume holds ideas that are practical and easily employed in any healing strategy. Long may this book be on the shelves.

Colin Griffith (September 2013)

Prologue

I have to pinch myself. I still can't believe that I am sitting on a beautiful sandy beach on a Greek island. I watch my young son play with his truck in the sand while waves gently lap at his feet. He and my partner are absorbed in the seemingly endless process of trying to fill a sandy well with water. They are so amused I find myself laughing and shaking my head while I reach over to peel a tasty orange. It is June 2013. I am currently in the final phase of my recovery from Chronic Fatigue Syndrome (CFS).

In April 2012 I had been diagnosed with a moderate to severe case of CFS and lay helpless in my bed. I was confused, terrified and very lonely. I was told to take things slowly (as if I had a choice) and offered anti-depressants as they were the only medication found to have been able to help some patients; but I was informed they did not really know how or why they helped. Well, I did not feel depressed as far as I could tell so I crawled into bed and stayed there. I got much worse before I began to feel any better. The mental, emotional and physical journeys I went on – and am still journeying through – have helped me to a) make sense of this particular illness, and b) finally understand what the Dalai Lama and other Eastern religious leaders have been trying to teach us, that the solution to any problem actually resides within ourselves.

To make sense of both I had to look back and work out how I got into such a state, and why. I was too weak to read, watch television or listen to music. My body ached for hours if I exerted myself even to lean over to drink some water. I was sensitive to sound and photophobic, thus having to wear earplugs and an eyemask twenty-four hours a day for around nine months. All I could do was think. What follows is a synopsis of my story and what I learnt from it and the treatments I found that helped me regain my health. I write this in the hope that it can help to relieve some of the panic and sense of helplessness that accompanies this illness. This illness is real, despite the unfortunate general perception that it is all in the mind, and it is a great challenge for both the sufferer and their family.

I wish you to keep faith that, given time, you will feel better. Please do not give up.

This book is dedicated to you.

My Chronic Fatigue Syndrome Experience:Timeline/ Summary

For many years I had been living at breakneck speed, multi-tasking to the nth degree and always putting my dreams on hold for a future I believed was never too far away. My friends would often ask me how I managed to do so many things at the same time, and in two different countries. In response, I would shrug my shoulders and answer that I honestly did not know. I felt as if I was on hyperdrive, and I had great difficulty slowing down. As you will discover in Chapter 2, this is a symptom of an overwhelmed Autonomic Nervous System (ANS), and in particular the vagal nerve. You will often hear that people who have collapsed with CFS used to have almost boundless energy; that is what makes it all the more shocking when they are no longer able to do things. In reality, all their energy reserves were being utilized while their body had no ability to self-regulate its balanced usage via the vagal complex system[1].

Before my collapse in March 2012 I had not slept well since the pregnancy and birth of my son in 2010. Also, I cared for my mother from 2005, who suffers from Rheumatoid Arthritis. In addition, I cared for my father from the end of December 2008 following his two strokes. He lived in Greece. I continued to hold down a part-time job, as well as start a company of my own organizing CPD talks for homeopaths and naturopaths.

Below is a summary of what I felt each month leading to and following my collapse.

September 2011

Fatigue begins. It feels as if my life force is slowly ebbing away. I can only describe it as 'someone suddenly pulled the plug'. Everything becomes very difficult to do. My legs feel so heavy that it is as if I am wading slowly upstream through a river.

October 2011

It feels harder and harder to get through the day and care for my 11-month-old son without help. I keep hoping that tomorrow I will feel better.

November 2011

I stop breast-feeding 'cold turkey', as my son only wants breast milk and will not switch to solids. He transitions well, but I feel very saddened by the break and have very swollen and painful breasts for five days until my body rebalances. I cancel a trip to Greece to see my father, as I do not feel strong enough to go.

December 2011

Go to in-laws for five days over Christmas. Not fun at all. I cannot sleep whilst here, and my first experience of sinusitis begins, which lasts for three to four weeks. Have builders working in our flat in London. It is stressful.

January 2012

Still have builders working on the flat. Second week in January and I get infected with Noro-virus after spending a sleepless night in

A&E with my son, who has developed a severe viral wheeze and has to be put on Ventolin.

January 21st – it feels as if someone has flipped a trip switch and my energy goes very low. I begin to spend most of my time in bed. I can move about the flat and make myself a sandwich if needed, but mostly I am in bed and read or watch television.

I find I am unable to sleep much at night.

February 2012

Second bout of Noro-virus or tummy bug. I have lost a lot of weight and look very pale and skinny. Any food I eat does not seem to be nourishing me. We move to our new flat end of February. I am unable to help with the move in any way.

March-April 2012

Collapse completely in bed. Unable to get up apart for the toilet and even that is a great struggle. After 16 days we finally call an ambulance and go to hospital. The paramedic makes it clear that he cannot work out what is wrong with me. I am pretty much ignored in the ambulance when I ask them to slow down. Worst of all, I see one paramedic tap his head, as if to say, 'It's all in her mind', when I am being admitted to the Emergency care doctors. All the tests they run on me are fine, and I am told to go on anti-depressants. I tell the doctor I do not feel depressed. 'Come back when you do,' I am told, 'then I will be able to help with that.' Not very encouraging, all in all. Even though I can barely stand or walk, the doctor at the hospital tells me to 'hop off' the bed and go home, and that I am fine. Within two weeks of the hospital visit I get much worse and cannot bathe nor feed myself. I cannot bear to be touched or spoken to. By mid-April I have lost my voice and can barely speak but for a whisper, I am wearing earplugs and an eye mask 24 hours a day unable to communicate or be with anyone. Not even my little boy. My only form of communication is short texts to my partner to say what I need. Then my partner sneaks into the room as quietly as possible and leaves what I need on my nightstand.

I cannot sleep day or night and can only lie in one position. My heartbeat is so slow it feels like it might just stop. Breathing is slow and shallow. It feels at times over a six-week period that I am slipping in and out of consciousness. I have to be fed practically every two hours. I cannot really taste what I eat and don't feel as if any nourishment remains in my body. There is a feeling of desperation to eat, as if I'm not able to metabolize anything properly. Despite the amount of food I consume I have lost a lot of weight and am actually severely under weight. I cannot feel my feet very well, and as I lie here I avoid looking down at them as they look jaundiced. Dead man's feet, I think. It is terrifying.

I manage, with a great deal of help and determination, to get myself each week to acupuncture. Although it has proven helpful for many with CFS, I don't really feel any benefit. I'm too terrified to stop, though, as I'm not sure at this point what I could do to help myself. As stress and overwork seem to be the cause of my condition, I ask if I'm suffering from extreme Adrenal Fatigue. My acupuncturist says it could be described like that. From his perspective, though, it is spleen and kidney chi deficiency. The discussion is not taken any further. I just do not understand what is wrong with me. I feel really frustrated. When will this end?

May-June 2012

I have three sessions with a Journey work[2] practitioner who comes to our home. I also begin Craniosacral therapy[3] at home, and begin homeopathic treatment[4]. After these treatments I slowly begin to feel something shift in the right direction.

It is end of June, I start to need less food at night – only two or three times between 9pm and 6am. Starting to sleep a bit more, though waking up every one to two hours.

July 2012

I am able to take my first tentative steps, though still confined to my bed. I manage to get to the living room, and there lie on the floor in the sun for ten minutes once a day. My feet are still very pale but not so deathly looking.

August 2012

I stop Craniosacral treatment, as I cannot afford it alongside acupuncture.

September 2012

Stop acupuncture, as I realize it is the Craniosacral that is better for me.

October-December 2012

Start Craniosacral again, and add Reiki[5]. From mid-November I also receive spiritual healing[6] at home.

November 2012

Sleep begins to take some shape. Am able to sleep three hours in a row at night, sometimes four. Also eating less, and am starting to put on some weight.

Christmas 2012

I wake up on December 22nd and I know there is something

different. It's as if my power mains has been switched back on. Within a week, I no longer need my earplugs and eye mask. Within a month, I can slowly spend some time in the living room (ten mins or so) lying on the couch with my partner and son in the room. Within six weeks I can sit up a bit. I describe it to my family: this illness makes you feel as if you're wearing a straight jacket or an impossibly large and heavy body suit.

I go from being virtually completely restricted in my movements to slowly, each week, feeling a loosening (so to speak) of the restrictive mobility. Up until mid-December 2012 the brain fog and my greatly reduced ability to process any sensory information made me feel totally at a loss, confused and cut off from the world. Now I feel I am back. I was so alone all these months. I just want to be with my family. I really need to be with my son again.

January 2013

My father suddenly gets ill and weak. I cannot see or speak to him except via a kind nurse, who puts her mobile to his ear. He doesn't sound great. I know it's bad. I lie there not knowing what to do. My heart aches; I have not seen him since September 2011. He is waiting for us to come for a visit to Greece now in January, but I'm still too weak to journey.

He steadily gets worse. He is rushed to hospital February 4th and dies on the 8th. His funeral is on the 11th and sadly I am unable to attend. There are no words to describe how I feel. I learn a big lesson in love, friendship and being able to rely on others from this. I am eternally grateful to our close family friends, who organize everything for me. My parents are only-children and I am also in essence an only-child. I have two half-brothers with whom I have no relationship, so I really had no one to turn to. So when my dad's closest friends and my closest friends take the lead to do everything, I am humbled by all their love and support.

February-April 2013

Each week I feel a bit stronger and more able to move about my room albeit very slowly. My partner begins to run a bath for me each evening, which feels like heaven. I walk up and down the flat. Watch some television. Cuddles with my son – at last! What joy! Each day a little more.

Eating and sleeping patterns begin to settle. Continue to put on weight.

I see my mom for the first time in many months. It makes my heart warm to see the relief on her face and to know she has been rooting for me even though she could not understand what was going on with me. She tried to visit with me when I was very ill but I just could not have her come in my room. I could barely stand having anyone in our flat, let alone anywhere near me. I realize at this point what a toll this illness takes on those nearest to me. My mom's eyes have changed. I'm told she cried a lot and felt helpless herself at not being able to be with me or to do something to help. I still cannot explain to her exactly what has happened to me nor how long it will be till I can do more than spend a few minutes at a time with her; but it's a nice feeling to be able to make a start.

May 10th 2013

Fly to Greece (with a great deal of assistance). I visit my father's grave. It all seems very surreal. On May 25th I take a boat to the Greek island of Patmos. All the staff at the airport and on the boat are so helpful. I'm taken everywhere by wheelchair and given such a lot of support. I realize I don't feel shy any more to ask for help, something I recognize now I had great difficulty in doing before.

Since arriving in Greece the heat seems to give me strength. Within days of arriving neighbours say they see a huge difference in me. I have to agree with them. I feel it. Being on the island by the sea is a tonic second to none. I am still unable to spend any length of time away from home, yet I feel like I have begun to slowly re-enter everyday living.

Eating and sleeping patterns have settled. I no longer eat during the night, and manage to sleep through with only one wake-up at around 3am. I am overweight, though it is beginning to go down.

June 2013

On Patmos. It is incredible to be on the beach. It's very quiet this time of year. Perfect for me. I feel amazing in the water.

End of June – I really feel I'm getting stronger and more able. I have one bad night after overdoing it for a couple of days, but recover within about three days.

July 2013

It's middle of July. There's been another shift upward. I am managing to hold a conversation now with people, if only for a few minutes at a time.

July 10th – Have bumped into an old friend and it feels good to be around her. I still need to rest and take it easy.

July 18th – Have my first lunch out in a café for 30 mins. Not easy at all, due to noise and a lot of movement around me, but feel a great achievement to be able to do it.

August 2013

There is another shift. From August 7th I feel a difference in my stamina and the amount of things I can do in between rests.

August 21st – I manage to go to a secluded beach that can only be reached by walking over a small hill. I had not realized it was quite so long (1.2km) nor that it was a steep path before I arrived, otherwise I would not have considered it. I manage it, though! I don't know how I'll make it back to the car but thankfully a kind fisherman takes pity on me and ferries me back to the place where we left the car. It's been such a confidence booster that I managed that trek and enjoyed two hours at the beautiful beach with my family.

I really feel I have recovered, and it is only a case of building stamina and being careful not to put myself in stressful or tiring situations. I don't feel ready to go back to work as yet, but the idea of it no longer seems impossible. Yay! I also feel ready to begin my trip back to Britain. Am happy to be able to head home.

August 28th – My book is pretty much complete. I'm astounded that I've managed to slowly put this together.

This whole process of falling ill, though, has been so transformative. Through it I gained a deeper understanding of my needs, and can see how my behavior towards myself and others has radically changed. As I improve mentally and physically, I feel as if I'm breaking free from the restrictive bonds that held me so tight. This experience has burned away the constraints of fear and social expectation I've always felt; by regaining my physical health, I now feel both physically and emotionally free to just be myself.

September 2013

It's mid-September, and we're back in London. After living on a small island and with such open space it doesn't feel very nice coming back to a city. Nor, if I'm honest, does it feel nice to enter back into the flat in which all I've known is pain and suffering. We had always planned to move to the countryside. Like everyone else, we talked about the day we would do it. Well, that day is now. We both realize very quickly that the city life is not for us.

I continue to pace myself and work on building up my confidence and stamina.

October 2013

We've sold our flat and found a small village to move to in East Sussex. We've found a new home and are now enjoying our time in London, as we know it will not be long till we move. I look into learning more on Reiki. I discover a course that I find appealing. I can do most of the studying at home, then go in for a one-day practical side, working with a small group. I email the course tutor and explain my situation and she assures me I will get all the support and space I need.

October 27th – I spend my first day away from home and manage to complete my requirements for Reiki I level. It's such a huge achievement for me. The first part of the course was a home study, but I chose to go in for the one-day practical course. The support I receive from the teacher and the other three who form part of the group is just what I need to get through the day. It couldn't have gone better, thank goodness. Not only do I benefit from all the energy work done, but also my confidence grows immensely by being able to be away from home for so many hours.

November 2013

Our son turns three. I am able to be with him this year!

It is amazing what joy I now experience with all the simple things in life that were easily overlooked or taken for granted before. If I ever feel myself getting impatient now I remind myself that each moment I can do something is a blessing and not to be taken for granted.

December 2013

I look forward to 2014! I will try to never take my health and well being for granted again.

January/February 2014

We're moving out of London. City life is not for us and our son. We move to East Sussex. What an amazingly beautiful place. The countryside just takes my breath away. I feel I have been given a second opportunity in life, and I intend to grab it with both hands.

March 2014

We've only just arrived and already I feel an immense difference in myself. Being in a different environment I think is helping me to regain my confidence and begin to do things as I did before falling ill. There are no bad memories linked to this place. I suppose there are no feelings of restriction or constant reminders of what I was unable to do only a few months ago. I think moving was the best idea ever.

April 2014

We are settling in to our new home and we have found a lovely pre-school for our son. The teachers are wonderful and I can see he feels secure in this environment and looks forward to going each morning. It is such a relief for me, as he has not had an easy time, having been separated from me during 2012. I can see in his eyes that he knows I will be there to pick him up in a few hours. The separation anxiety I noticed is subsiding.

May-July 2014

Life has taken on a sense of normality. I feel ready to say goodbye to CFS once and for all. I am ready to move forward without fear or worry.

Notes

1   Forms part of our Autonomic Nervous System; in particular the feedback loop between the Sympathetic and Parasympathetic Nervous Systems when in our fight, flight or immobilize response mode. Explained in Chapter 2.

2   A therapy helping to deal with psychological issues described in Tier 2 of Chapter 5.

3   An alternative treatment described in Tier 1, Chapter 5.

4   An alternative form of medical treatment, described in Tier 1, Chapter 5.

5   Energy, hands-on healing described in Tier 1, Chapter 5.

6   Energy healing – Tier 1, Chapter 5.

CHAPTER 1

What is health? What is disease?

Before describing my theory on CFS and how it develops I would just like to say a few words on what constitutes health and disease from a holistic perspective. Health is when the body can adapt to stimuli around it, such as a change in the weather or emotional upset, by bringing itself back to balance. Disease ('dis-ease') is when the body is unable to do so. When there is a sudden imbalance that takes a few days to resolve it is referred to as an acute disease. An acute disease can be either mild or very intense, even in some cases resulting in death. When an imbalance develops over a number of months or years it is referred to as a chronic disease. Chronic disease tends to affect our lives bit by bit and we adjust to it without even realizing in most cases.

Have you ever pondered what symptoms actually are? I never had. It was not until the last ten years that I realized that symptoms are not the problem but simply road signs pointing toward the underlying cause of disease. Symptoms are in fact the body's only way of communicating what is going on beneath the surface. It is quite a revelation when you begin to see symptoms as allies rather than something that need to be got rid of as quickly as possible. For example, imagine you had a raging fire in your belly and smoke was billowing out of your ears and nostrils. The symptom in this case is the smoke, and the body's disease a raging fire. If you were able to put small corks in the nostrils and earplugs to stop the symptom (smoke) you may succeed in doing so, but the fire will still rage within. The body will then need to find a different way (symptom) to make you aware there is still an underlying problem. It may do so by causing you to double up in pain and feel a burning sensation in your belly. If you take a pain killer and antacid, once again you will rid yourself of your symptoms but not of the underlying disease. The body will continue to look for ways to ask for help.

The longer it goes unrecognized, the more damage is caused. What started off as an isolated fire may begin to spread to the rest of the system, causing more problems and more symptoms. Thus, like a detective, it is best to look at symptoms as clues to a puzzle and work your way back to the cause of disease and discomfort in your body. In the case of CFS, I believe it is a chronic disease that for some develops over months, while for others it could be over a number of years. It is described as a multi-system and multi-causal disease with a myriad of symptoms, yet if you deconstruct it, and look at what lies beneath, to where the symptoms are pointing, it suddenly all becomes quite clear. Though there is no quick fix, there is a way for us to overcome this illness.

Discoveries of CFS Research:

- A large number of CFS patients suffer from low cardiac output (low blood supply going around the body). It has been found that CFS patients have almost normal levels of cardiac output when lying down but when they stand up it lowers rather than rising to meet the increased metabolic demand. For some with CFS the cardiac output is so low when they sit or stand up that it borders on heart failure. Cardiac insufficiency is one theory that has been put forward for people suffering from CFS.
- CFS patients suffer from cellular hypoxia (lack of oxygen, usually caused by an insufficient amount of oxygen being

circulated by the blood, which can result from low cardiac output);

- Respiration rate is affected in CFS patients (it slows down);
- CFS patients tend to suffer from hypoglycaemia (low blood sugar);
- CFS patients suffer from high system toxicity (as the liver is under-functioning and has a hard time detoxing the blood);
- CFS patients suffer from inefficient digestion and as a result malabsorption (whereby nutrients are not efficiently absorbed/assimilated into the system), which results in malnutrition);
- CFS patients suffer from inexplicable weight gain and loss (though inefficient digestion may hold the key to understanding that symptom);
- CFS patients have poor mitochondrial function (mitochondria are known as the energy generators of each cell. They process fuel and oxygen to produce this energy we require to function as a whole);
- CFS patients have great trouble sleeping;
- CFS patients suffer from mood swings, though it has been clinically found that depression is not a causal factor of CFS. CFS patients get depressed as a result of their illness, when there seems to be no light at the end of the tunnel.
- CFS patients' brain scans show impaired blood supply to certain areas of the brain. Studies show that hypoperfusion (reduced cerebral blood flow) is prevalent among sufferers;
- CFS patients' brain functional scans have been described as closely resembling those of patients who have experienced a stroke.

The signs and symptoms experienced by CFS patients are extensive and differ in severity from person to person. They can include the inability to move, multi-task, think clearly or sleep well. There can be tremendous pain in the limbs in the muscles upon exertion that can linger. Some people feel nauseous and faint, and many have digestion issues. The list goes on (and often seems endless) but I have included two links at the back of the book where you can look at the criteria that UK and Canada use for diagnosing CFS. It is important to remember that chronic fatigue is simply one of many symptoms, and for some patients not necessarily a severely debilitating one. The word 'syndrome' is used to describe a collection of symptoms of unknown causation but which occur together regularly in a number of sufferers. Attempts have been made to change the name from 'CFS' to something more representative of this illness, as it has been found inadequate; studies have shown that people respond with less or more seriousness to the nature of the illness depending on the name used to describe it. Other names by which CFS is referred to is ME (Myalgic Encephalomyelitis), Post-Viral Fatigue Syndrome, NDS (Neuroendocrineimmune Dysfunction Syndrome), and CFIDS (Chronic Fatigue and Immune Dysfunction Syndrome).

Okay. So, having established all this, my questions were: Why are we experiencing all these symptoms? Why is cardiac output low? Why are the mitochondria under-functioning? Some argue that one is the reason for the other, a sort of chicken-and-egg argument. Yet, we know the body works in a logical and efficient manner, therefore there has to be something that brings everything into perspective. For my peace of mind I needed to understand why and how this illness develops. I honestly thought the answer was already out there, but I soon discovered it was not. By pure chance I had an unexpected insight that came to me whilst reading a particular study on the vagal complex system within the Autonomic Nervous System (ANS); I realized that this study put into perspective all the other research and theory proposals I had read regarding this illness. Based on this insight, I propose that CFS is a malfunction of the tenth cranial nerve, the vagus nerve, as a result of too much pressure (stress) over a sustained period of time.

Acronyms

ANS – Autonomic Nervous System
AF – Adrenal Fatigue
CFS – Chronic Fatigue Syndrome
CFIDS – Chronic Fatigue and Immune Dysfunction Syndrome
CNS – Central Nervous System
EFT – Emotional Freedom Technique
GAD – Generalized Anxiety Disorder
HBOT – Hyperbaric Oxygen Therapy
ME – Myalgic Encephalomyelitis
NDS – Neuroendocrineimmune Dysfunction Syndrome
PNS – Parasympathetic Nervous System
OCD – Obsessive Compulsive Disorder
SNDS– Sympathetic Nervous System
VN – Vagus Nerve
VNS – Vagus Nerve Stimulation

CHAPTER 2

Chronic Fatigue Syndrome (CFS). How it develops

When I was in my late teens/early twenties I was fascinated by human behaviour, what it is that makes each person tick, why one person will react to a situation in one manner, whilst someone else will have a completely different or opposing response. I wanted to understand Freud's theory on the id, ego and superego. I was enamored with Carl Rogers and his humanistic approach. When it came to the brain, our development and subconscious, I was absolutely absorbed by anything I could read on the subject. So, in due course, I went to university in Athens to study Psychology. I loved every minute of it. We had to take certain compulsory physiology and anatomy modules, and I remember three of us begging our anatomy and physiology professor to do a module on neurobiology and physiology. After a couple of semesters of presenting our thoughts to her and the university our wish was granted. We had the A&P lab to ourselves and our professor took full advantage of the small group size to allow us the opportunity of doing in-depth theory and practical study.

After the second year I applied and was offered a scholarship to study psychology in London, an opportunity I grabbed with both hands. Whilst studying in London, I had a flatmate doing a course on homeopathy. I did not really understand what homeopathy was and admittedly I didn't give it much credence when she explained it to me. In fact, I initially dismissed it. Two years later, and we were both doing our respective student clinics and seeing patients. By this time I had tried a couple of remedies and had been pleasantly surprised by their effectiveness. We discussed certain ailments, in particular Obsessive Compulsive Disorder (OCD) and Generalized Anxiety Disorder (GAD) and what approaches we each used to help a patient overcome them. In the months that followed our initial discussions, I observed the patient recovery feedback and was astonished by how effective the homeopathic treatment appeared to be.

After my graduation I began to look into homeopathy to try and understand it. I had an idea I could perhaps incorporate it in to my psychological therapeutic process to provide clients with the best of both. I soon discovered that psychology already formed a great part of the homeopathic case-taking, and was given due consideration when deciding on what remedy a patient would best benefit from. After weighing it up carefully I decided it would best serve my patients if I also did a degree in homeopathy. After almost five years of studying psychology I wasn't too keen to do another four years at a desk, but I did. It was the best thing I could have done; I was introduced to a more holistic approach to understanding and treating health and disease. Also what we as practitioners can do to empower a person to help themselves. From 2005 I completely immersed myself in the world of homeopathy, studying at the College for Homeopathic Education and working within a homeopathic pharmacy.

I felt happy overall, though I secretly suffered from a great deal of anxiety and from an inability to ask for help when I felt tired or overwhelmed. Anxiety was something I had suffered from since I was very young, and now realize that I simply learned to live with it. Things would upset or worry me but I never expressed it. I thought I could resolve most things on my own, given time, yet as the years went by it felt as if I were carrying a backpack filled with rocks, each rock representing an unresolved issue. When my parents became ill, I got pregnant, and I continued to work until it finally all caught up with me in 2011/2012. I collapsed. The irony was not lost on me here; I had spend most of my adult life focusing on how to help others, and as I lay helpless in bed it began to dawn on me that I had never really looked at what I could do to address my own needs. Nor had I ever looked at what help I needed in my life.

When I began to recover and was able to start reading a little bit more (from March 2013) I was determined to try and work out what had happened to me. What was CFS actually all about? I had heard about it before collapsing but I just thought it was a case of someone feeling really, really exhausted. It was also confusing, as CFS and Myalgic Encephalomyelitis (ME) were disease names used interchangeably to describe what appeared to be the same thing.

The motivation to write this book arose because, even with my experience of homeopathy and psychology, I could not understand what was happening to my body and mind, or why. I could not understand why I was not recovering at all despite lying in bed for hours, days and weeks on end. I could not understand why I found it virtually impossible to structure a sentence, hold a short conversation or understand when spoken to. In short, I could not understand how I had become such a physical and mental wreck. I was thrown into this nightmare illness and my journey was to find a way to overcome and understand it. I eventually made it, and now with all that I have experienced and discovered through reading, I understand it. This is what I would like to share with you in this little book, to give you hope through understanding and recommend some tools for you to help yourself.

In this chapter and the following I will outline the information and research that helped me to understand how and why this illness develops. I will not touch upon nor include the numerous research studies that exist on CFS/ME, though at some point you may want to read them. I wish to focus primarily on the information and research study that underpin my theory on the development of CFS.

The best description of CFS I have heard is that it is as if a person's hard drive has collapsed, and I now believe this to be very perceptive. The obvious question is, 'But how does this happen?'

In brief, CFS develops as follows:

* Exposure to prolonged or repeated stress(ors), severe shock, and/or unresolved trauma which affects the immune system, and the Sympathetic/Parasympathetic Nervous System. All of which make up the Autonomic Nervous System (ANS);
* Inherited Sympathetic Nervous System overload (epigenetics) – Chapter 3;
* Inefficient coping strategies (learnt behaviour) – Chapter 3;
* Different response to stress according to sex (innate response) – Chapter 3;
* Prolonged adrenal gland function, 'fight or flight' response, which leads to Adrenal Fatigue (AF);
* Prolonged AF eventually affects the function of the vagus nerve (vagal complex feedback loop), which forms part of the ANS, resulting in a collection of signs and symptoms known as CFS.

Below I will outline how this unfolds.

Stress and Adrenal Fatigue

In the summer of 2012, I did begin to wonder if perhaps my adrenals were affected due to the stress load I had been carrying for a number of years and the anxiety of it all. I was unable to confirm my suspicion that this was indeed the case until I got a lot better.

The adrenals, which are situated above the kidneys, secrete steroid hormones in response to any changes that occur in our emotional, physical and psychological environment. They form part of our system's 'fight or flight' response to perceived (possible) danger.

AF (Adrenal Fatigue), a term coined by Dr. James L. Wilson[7] in 1998, is caused by stress overload; any stressor (see Table 1) or combination of stressors, whether very intense or experienced over a prolonged period of time, can deplete our adrenal function and lead to AF. Adrenals respond to all stress in the same manner and at the same level. So, for example, whether we are being chased by a tiger, stuck in a traffic jam or caring for a terminally-ill loved one, it will elicit the same response from the adrenals and therefore have the same impact on the body. AF is clinically referred to as hypoadrenia. It is also known as adrenal apathy ('apathy' is from the Greek word apatheia meaning 'without feeling' or 'non-responsive'), and adrenal neurasthenia ('neura' is Greek for 'nerves', and 'asthenia' means ailment). I do find these last two descriptions very interesting when connecting them with the eventual development of CFS.

STRESSORS		
Accidents	Wounds	Feeling trapped
Allergies	Toxins	Feeling pressured (external or self-inflicted)
Smoking	Viral Infections	Decision Fatigue – brain on constant alert – no rest from decision making

STRESSORS (continued)		
Coffee	Prescription drugs	Anxiety
Lack of nutritious food	Recreational drugs	Fear
Bad eating habits	Lack of exercise/too much exercise	Death of loved one; Any severe emotional shock
Bad sleeping habits	Over-exerting self	Marriage failing
Inability to relax	Pessimistic outlook	Financial pressures
Inability to say 'No' (boundary issue)	Feeling over-responsible for others (boundary issue)	Putting others' needs before one's own (boundary issue)

Table 1: Stressors and trauma that affect the ANS and may lead to AF and CFS. There are a number of other stressors, though, that are unique to the individual. What is stressful for one person might be a source of fun for another (ie loud music), so this list is not exhaustive, but an indication of what you need to begin to be aware of when examining your life and what is having a negative impact on your wellbeing.

The section below is a mix of paraphrasing/summarising and direct quotation of the main symptoms of Adrenal Fatigue, and key findings (with permission) from Dr. Wilson's book Adrenal Fatigue: The 21st Century Stress Syndrome (2001):

- Great difficulty in getting up in the morning
- Continuing fatigue that is not relieved by sleep
- Craving for salt or salty foods
- Lack of energy (lethargy) – everything feels like a chore, even things you consider fun
- Increased effort to do every day tasks
- Decreased sex drive
- Decreased ability to handle stress
- Increased time needed to recover from illness, injury or emotional trauma
- Mild depression. Less enjoyment or happiness with life
- Increased PMS (Pre-Menstrual Stress)
- Symptoms increase if meals are skipped or inadequate (hypoglycaemia)
- Thoughts less focused, more fuzzy
- Memory less accurate
- Decreased tolerance – easily irritated by others or tasks
- Do not really feel awake till 10am
- Afternoon low between 3:00 and 4:00pm
- Feel better after evening meal
- Interrupted sleep. Waking around 3am with difficulty falling back to sleep
- Decreased productivity – takes longer to do tasks. Difficulty multi-tasking

If a person is experiencing three or more of the symptoms outlined above there is a very good chance they are suffering from AF. AF occurs along a spectrum whereby in severe cases a person can barely get up out of bed for more than a certain amount of time per day. The more fatigued the adrenal function is, the more every organ and system within our body is affected. Interestingly, although AF has been researched and documented since the early 1900s, in the last 40 odd years it has become under-diagnosed. This is because it is an illness that cannot readily be treated by prescription drugs, as it is not easily categorized as a disease by the medical profession and pharmaceutical companies. As such, it is an ailment that is now very much overlooked by doctors. It is estimated that due to our current lifestyle(s) a vast number of the population (over 70%) is already suffering from or has experienced some level of AF.

AF appears to be a precursor to other seemingly unrelated ailments and diseases. For example, most people with AF develop physical symptoms such as hypoglycaemia (low blood sugar levels), Pre-Menstrual Stress (PMS), depressed immune function, various allergies, food sensitivities and insomnia. On a mental/emotional level they develop symptoms that include: anxiety, fears, phobias, depression, brain fog, weak memory and difficulty in concentrating. They can get very easily irritated or frustrated as they tire quickly. If AF is left untreated things often get worse, leading to more chronic conditions such as asthma, recurring respiratory infections, frequent colds, sinusitis and viral infections. Going to an even deeper level of disease, AF can be observed as having laid the foundation for a number of chronic health problems such as auto-immune disorders (ie Lupus or Rheumatoid Arthritis), Fibromyalgia, Type II Diabetes, and CFS.

There is a point following which an individual suffering from AF will develop one of the major health problems mentioned above. Why exactly one person gets Fibromyalgia and another CFS may be simply due to their individual experience dictated by their hereditary make-up and general susceptibility to illness.

I had quite a few of the symptoms listed above, and I have no doubt I was suffering from AF for a number of years, with symptoms building since my mid-teens. I believe a heavy stress load between 2004 and 2011 led to my eventual collapse from CFS.

The Polyvagal Theory: Social Engagement System

As I began to recover in 2013 I started to download as much information as I could on CFS. I read books and research findings. I found when going through the research that it felt similar to when you miss the first few minutes of a film, whereby you spend a lot of time and effort trying to work out what is going on but still feel you are missing that key bit of information that brings it all together. Then, a particular scene occurs or an actor makes a statement that brings the whole picture into perspective, and you relax. That is how I felt when I came across information regarding AF, as well as research conducted by Dr. Stephen W. Porges[8] in 1995 on the vagus nerve located in our brain.

For those who develop CFS I believe it is damage to the vagus nerve function that results in virtually every system of the body being affected. The vagus nerve originates in the brain and then branches out as far as our abdomen. It is the longest of all cranial nerves, whose function has evolved to take on an increasingly complex role in our response to the environment; in brief, the vagus nerve is connected to the cranium, face and neck and to key organs in the chest and abdomen (heart, lungs, liver and stomach). It forms part of our ANS, described further on, and is key in keeping our heart rate constant and controlling food digestion.

The brain has three parts to it (see Table 2), which evolved over time in the following order: the Basal Brain (reptilian brain), the Limbic System (mammalian brain), and the Neocortex (human brain).

- The Basal Brain is all about instinct and survival.
- The Limbic System deals with our emotional life, also in response to our survival needs.

- The Neocortex has a right and left hemisphere and is responsible for our creativity and intellect respectively. It is also where the sensory and motor regions are located. It is what differentiates us from other mammals, what makes us human.

The three parts of the brain do not operate independently of each other. They are interconnected via numerous neural pathways. As I will show through Dr. Porges' work, The Polyvagal Theory, such neural connections are key to understanding the development and symptom picture of CFS.

Table 2 (overleaf): A brief description of the evolution of the brain from its reptilian roots to include the Limbic and Neocortex (Tatkin, 2011; Porges, 2011).

In his *Polyvagal Theory*, Dr. Porges describes how two vagal systems have evolved. The two systems, the Dorsal Motor Vagal Complex ('dumb vagus') and the Ventral Vagal Complex ('smart vagus') located in the medulla oblongata of the reptilian part of our brain, have been programmed with different response strategies, and as such they have been found to be able to respond in a contradictory manner in the same organ.

As the brain evolved to allow for the more complicated human behaviour it created new circuitry to run alongside the old, rather than replace it. So, in the reptilian part of your brain you find that the 'dumb' vagus is hardwired to produce responses that are better suited to the survival of a reptile, not humans. A reptile reacts purely from instinct and operates predominantly on an unconscious level, and our very swift-acting survival mechanism triggered by emotional injury, physical trauma or threat, has us run, fight or freeze (shut down).

Humans and reptiles have the same initial reflexive response to any new situation, called the orienting reflex, which is key to our 'fight or flight' mechanism. However, humans have additional

The Brain	Development	Primary functions		Action	Main structural components
Reptilian	Oldest part of brain	Its primary concern is with our survival	Controls vital body functions such as balance, heart rate, breathing and body temperature	It is very reliable, but can be compulsive and rigid in its response	Includes the midbrain, pons and medulla oblongata. The medulla is where the 'dumb vagus', and 'smart vagus' originate
Limbic (Mammalian)	Developed in the first mammals. Located on top of brainstem and under the cortex	It is responsible for our emotional existence, particularly in relation to our survival	It records memories of behaviours that produced agreeable or disagreeable experiences	It acts very swiftly and is where we make value judgements, consciously and unconsciously, that influence our behaviour. Also swift actions related to our survival 'fight/flight'. Triggered by 'dumb vagus'	The amygdalae, hippocampus, cingulate gyrus (CG)[9], thalamus[10], and hypothalamus
Neocortex (Human)	Developed in primates, evolving into the human brain with two large cerebral hemispheres	It is here we developed our capacity for creativity, human language, imagination and consciousness	It is the part of the brain that allows us to create and sustain relationships. Social Engagement System	It is very flexible and has immense learning capabilities. Responds to environment more slowly than the Limbic System. Triggered by the 'smart vagus'	The right brain, left brain, orbitofrontal cortex and insula

behaviours, catered to by the 'smart' vagus, known as the Social Engagement System. This Social Engagement System allows us to decide whether to leave or remain in a situation and communicate. The smart vagus, by engaging our Neocortex, allows us to interact harmoniously in our environment and also enables us to create and maintain relationships with other people. It is this part of the brain that will establish whether or not any threats picked up by the dumb vagus need to be acted upon or disregarded. If a threat is to be ignored then the Neocortex will help to diffuse the situation by having the dumb vagus stand down.

Neuroscientists have found that our emotional response to a situation in the Limbic System is always much faster than our rational mind can keep up with, because the initial trigger is from the dumb vagus. The 'smart' vagus works more slowly because it has to process carefully all the sensory information to establish what is going on around us. In his research, Dr. Porges shows how the dumb and smart vagi work together (vagal complex system) via the ANS to maintain a balance in our response to our environment. In other words, the Limbic System, our emotional state and response to the environment is kept in balance by the smart and dumb vagi working in harmony.

The ANS (see table 3) regulates physiologically the function of our internal responses. 'Autonomo' is the Greek word for 'independent', and as such the ANS functions involuntarily and reflexively, having a direct affect on our heart, stomach, intestines and certain muscles within the body. It is the ANS that is activated in 'fight or flight' emergency situations, and also to relax the body 'rest and digest' in non-emergency situations by the vagal complex system. This feedback loop short-circuits in a CFS patient and needs to be given time to rebalance itself. Rebalancing this automated feedback loop is a slow process that occurs at its own pace on a physiological level; as such, we are unable to control it. In the treatment section, though, I have noted a number of strategies that can be used to help and support the process of recovery. Particularly,

AUTONOMIC NERVOUS SYSTEM		
Sympathetic Nervous System	Parasympathetic Nervous System	Enteric Nervous System
Prepares system for action	Relaxes the body, induces healing	Regulates normal activity of the digestive system
Speeds up heart rate	Slows heart rate	Contains extensive neural circuits capable of local autonomic function
Constricts blood vessels	Relaxes blood vessels	It has a two-way connection to Central Nervous System
Stimulates the release of stress hormones		Referred to as 'second brain' due to the extent of its functioning and the degree of autonomy it works with
		90% of fibers of the vagus nerve carry information from the gut to the brain

Table 3: Autonomic Nervous System (Marieb, 2006)

during your recovery it is imperative (as much as possible) to keep yourself out of stimulating environments so as not to trigger the ANS 'fight or flight' or its 'immobilize' response.

In humans the attention and emotion required for the Social Engagement System to come into play makes the heart work a lot harder, so our energy production is much greater than that of reptiles. In fact, "mammals have metabolic demands four to five times that of a reptile" (Porges, 2011). Dr. Porges uses the car for an analogy, explaining that "reptiles locomote with a reliable but underpowered engine and mammals locomote with a supercharged engine that can function for only short periods of time without refueling" (Porges, 2011).

Adapting to our different metabolic requirements makes us use different vagal strategies to promote our survival. This is important to note when relating this information to the development of CFS. In humans, there is a 'vagal brake' on the heart to control energy output so we do not bounce off the walls due to high-energy release and thus deplete it. Reptiles, on the other hand, do not produce the high levels of energy we do, so the vagal brake is released on their heart in order to allow them to function. Otherwise, they would grind to a halt.

In humans, the vagal brake is automatically withdrawn in response to external demands where we need more energy output, such as exercise, stress, attention and information processing. This means that when we have a lot of demands placed on us we require more energy, and therefore our vagal complex system will release the brake to allow output to increase. If this occurs regularly or continuously, as in high stress situations, the 'brake on–off' system begins to malfunction, staying in the 'off' position, and our energy stores begin to deplete. When this happens pathological and antisocial patterns of behaviour arise, such as hyperactivity, irritability, impatience and rage. Scientists measuring the vagal brake find it virtually non-existent in instances of rage and hyperactivity.

Such emotional and behavioral outbursts without the ability for conscious self-regulation have been labelled 'reptilian'. An example of this would be a person's inability to take constructive comments on board without over-reacting by getting angry, being aggressive and taking it very personally, with the possibility of inner thoughts of retribution.

If we do not ease off and allow the smart vagus a chance to relax our system by turning on the vagal brake, then the signs and symptoms of CFS will begin to appear as our body's energy stores are depleted and unable to replenish. A vagal brake stuck in the 'reptilian brake-off' mode is potentially lethal to us. Reptiles are built not to be as oxygen-dependent as we are; they do not require the same amount of energy to perform their metabolic requirements.

Having a depleting or depleted energy system, as well as being stuck in the reptilian brake-off mode when entering into a novel situation, means we will not have the energy output we need to engage either our 'fight or flight' mode or our Social Engagement behaviours. Being in this reptilian mode means our oxygen resources are too low for us to function properly and results in the following:

- Our Central Nervous System (CNS) begins to under-function. This results in great difficulty for us to process sensory information – leading to sensory overload. We therefore struggle to process any internal and external demands;
- It becomes difficult to do more than one thing at a time and for some it can be impossible to multi-task. There is an overall reduction in behavioral complexity. It becomes increasingly difficult to go through the decision making process and put things in to action;
- Unconsciousness has also resulted in some cases due to the decreased oxygen levels;

- When not enough oxygen is circulating the body then vital organs begin to under function, but will eventually be damaged in the long run. In severe cases it could result in death.

These are all aspects of a damaged ANS feedback loop that could explain the myriad of signs and symptoms experienced by CFS sufferers. For mammals, it is vital to increase metabolic output in order to be able to display our 'fight or flight' behaviours. Therefore, if our human response to a novel situation is unable to kick in, we are rendered helpless, weak and in a paralytic state. It is quite difficult to accept how vulnerable we actually are in this situation but we need to understand it either to avoid or overcome it. It is vital to know that our Neocortex is very defenseless to shifts in oxygen. Our ANS strategies have evolved to make sure there is the right amount of oxygen available to the brain at all times. However, since our human strategies coexist with our ancestral reptilian strategies we need to be very careful not to get overwhelmed or the system will eventually malfunction.

Avoiding being overwhelmed is about understanding how our brain circuitry has evolved and how it responds to things. Dr. Porges' research shows that systems of the brain react to challenges in a hierarchical manner, and not in a balanced one. The response is based on the evolution of the vagal complex and the ANS overall from reptiles to mammals to human beings.

The hierarchy of our neural circuits and how they react is as follows:

- We enter into a novel situation or an existing stressful situation and we initially react with the orienting reflex (dumb vagus) followed by the Social Engagement System (smart vagus); this is the newest system to evolve in the brain, in order to engage with our environment, soothe ourselves and promote a calm state.
- If our Neocortex is unable to deal with the situation, our brain

will naturally have to remain with the initial dumb vagus response, which triggers our 'fight or flight' response (Limbic System). If this mobilization response begins to falter or fail...

• Then we fall back on our oldest system of vagal operation, the immobilization response; this is when the dumb vagus, as a last resort, will trigger the 'freeze' or 'shut down' systems.

The freeze-immobilize system is potentially lethal for us. It is an involuntary defense response in which the mammal 'pretends' to die; its pain threshold is raised and it finds itself in a dissociative state. This can be triggered in humans if they are overwhelmed. What we observe is "behavioral shutdown, frequently accompanied by very weak muscle tone. We also observe physiological changes: heart rate and breathing slow, and blood pressure drops." If there is an element of fear involved as well, then it "elicits profound, potentially lethal, physiological changes (ie, dramatic slowing of heart rate, cessation of breathing, and dropping of blood pressure)" (Porges, 2011). When experiencing a nervous system disorder (neuropathology) some people may lose altogether the ability to work out if an environment is safe or not. If a person feels fear and 'trapped' in any situation, unable to see a way out, then this mindset can eventually overwhelm the system, moving past the self-soothe mode, past 'fight or flight' and in to the immobilization mode. Bringing this into clear perspective, CFS happens when the body has overwhelmed the Social Engagement System, has also exhausted the 'fight nor flight' systemic (emotional) response, resulting in the freeze response. This means our body is shut down as a survival mechanism when the Neocortex has become too overwhelmed to process sensory information and provide the necessary feedback that allows the Limbic brain to calm down following a stress-related situation or survival alert. In sum, there is a short circuit between the feedback loop between the dumb and smart vagi. Obviously this is a life-threatening position to find oneself in. How is our body able to shut us down? What does this mean? It means the vagus nerve will slow down our heartbeat – it is our heart's pacemaker's pacemaker so to speak, so it results in low cardiac output. It also affects our respiration rate as it is able to constrict our bronchi. As this nerve is also able to directly affect our stomach and liver functions we have a reduction in our overall metabolic function. This will have a knock-on effect whereby not enough oxygen and fuel will be circulated around the blood, so the mitochondria in our cells will be unable to produce the energy we require.

Low cardiac output has a huge impact on our capacity to be mobile, as it has to do with the amount (volume) of blood that is pumped out of the heart every minute. A normal cardiac output is about five litres at rest, which goes up with exercise and movement. When our heart rate is either too low or too fast it has the same effect, by reducing cardiac output. I found out that "as a general rule, a patient with a heart rate that is too fast (>150/minute – the heart does not have enough filling time) or too slow (<50/minute – not enough rate for heart to fill) requires urgent assessment for signs and symptoms of shock. Both extreme rates can be associated with inadequate cardiac output. Signs and symptoms of shock include shortness of breath, chest pains, hypotension, and an altered level of consciousness (due to hemodynamic compromise)" (Barill, 2007). This is extremely important to consider. Could it be that CFS is the ultimate Stress Disorder or Post Traumatic Stress Disorder and that our body is stuck in what could be described as a chronic state of shock or trauma?

Though all this sounds quite frightening, it also gives what I have found to be the most plausible explanation to what occurs pathologically or neurophysiologically to a person diagnosed with CFS. This to me is good news; by understanding the condition a person is able to take the necessary steps to overcome it. Furthermore, as the condition takes quite some time to develop, if you alter your lifestyle and seek appropriate treatment, you can make a full recovery.

What do you look for if you are worried that you or a loved one may have CFS? Early signs of CFS development can be observed in individuals suffering from generalized anxiety, fears, phobias, irritability, loss of joy and mild depression on the emotional side, whilst also exhibiting physiological symptoms such as sleeplessness, hypoglycemia and Irritable Bowel Syndrome, amongst others. So, basically, AF.

Unfortunately these symptoms are becoming accepted as the norm in society these days. Our fast-paced, competitive lifestyles have us accepting stress as a given and the disease we feel as a result of stress as something 'we just have to live with'. Well, the reality is that we actually do have a choice, though many would try to make us believe otherwise. If these initial symptoms are ignored and left unaddressed then the ANS will go into high alert and eventually become overwhelmed, thereby leaving the reptilian brain no choice but to shut down the body and leading to the myriad of symptoms associated with CFS. Like AF, CFS occurs along a spectrum of mild to very severe. In mild cases individuals have good and bad days, whereby with proper care of themselves and pacing they can interact with others and get on with their lives, although in a restricted form. In severe cases people are paralyzed in bed, unable to care for themselves or interact with anyone for any length of time, if at all. If left untreated, AF and CFS may last for a number of years. I believe that proper understanding of these conditions will allow you to take stock and change your lifestyle, incorporate proper care and treatment so that a full recovery can be made within one to three years, depending on the severity of the case.

I would like to add one last thought to this chapter about viral infections and CFS. CFS is basically a neurological disorder, meaning a sufferer's nervous system and as a consequence their immune system are left under-functioning quite dramatically. Therefore, viruses can easily affect you or resurface (in the case of a retrovirus), as the immune system is easily overwhelmed.

Researchers are trying to link CFS to a viral or bacterial infection but I now believe there is no one cause for CFS. There are as many triggers for this disease as there are people. Viruses, bacteria and toxins are the easiest to point fingers at because even in a robust individual they can compromise and overwhelm the physical body quite dramatically. In this case they are simply the 'straw that broke the camel's back'.

I have concluded that what needs to be understood is what came first – the systemic neurological weakness built from years of lack of strategy and structure to successfully function in a complex, highly-demanding modern world.

So, you can view CFS as not something you have contracted, but as a disease that developed over time.

Notes

7   Dr. James L. Wilson is acknowledged as an expert on alternative medicine, especially in the area of stress and adrenal function.

8   Dr. Stephen W. Porges is a Professor of Psychiatry conducting research at RTI in North Carolina.

9   The CG is involved with the regulation of aggressive behaviour and with sensory input concerning emotions.

10   The thalamus is involved in sensory perception and regulation of motor functions (such as movements), connecting areas of the cerebral cortex that are also involved in sensory perception and movement with other parts of the brain and spinal cord that also have a role in sensation and movement.

Key points from Chapter 2

- Stress and worry fill your life or you live in a stressful environment or situation. Stress is pressure. Stress is a term used to describe anything that puts pressure on you as an individual physically, mentally and/or emotionally.
- You begin to have no real downtime and feel little or no joy in life, or simply feel unable to escape a situation.
- Stress levels are higher than normal and more prolonged. The adrenal glands begin to tire from the exertion. Adrenal Fatigue (AF) begins to set in. A number of symptoms are experienced.
- If the AF symptoms are not addressed, your life begins to contract; everything seems a lot harder to deal with.
- At some point you suddenly feel as though your energy is severely depleted and not recovering. Everything begins to feel like a chore. You don't feel safe or that you can relax in any environment, sometimes not even at home alone. Your immune system is struggling as you begin to develop viral and bacterial infections.
- Once this occurs it signals that the smart vagus has become overwhelmed. The smart vagus working with our Neocortex uses what is called a Social Engagement System to calm us down and turn off our stress response. It is self-soothing, calming, and allows us to be metabolically efficient. So when this aspect is overwhelmed, our stress/relax feedback loop short-circuits.
- This is when the dumb vagus ends up being on constant alert; it remains triggered and on high alert even when not required. When we find ourselves in any new or potentially threatening situation the dumb vagus will trigger the Sympathetic Nervous System to turn on the 'fight or flight' mobilization system. The immune system too will be on high alert and over reacting (hence allergies and auto-immune disorders may develop).

- If this heightened state of alert is prolonged, the dumb vagus will, as a last resort, trigger the freeze–immobilize system. This will occur when this vagus complex and feedback loop is out of sorts, so that every system of the body is affected and a person experiences CFS.

The Autonomic Nervous System response

➢ Autonomic Nervous System (ANS) constantly monitors the environment and triggers our Sympathetic Nervous System (SNS) via the dumb vagus. It stimulates the nervous system to react.

➢ The SNS uses two systems to respond to the environment: the Hypothalamus-Pituitary-Adrenals axis (HPA axis) to respond to external threats, and the immune system which deals with internal threats such as bacterial or viral infection.

➢ The ANS triggers our Social Engagement System via the smart vagus.

➢ The Social Engagement System forms part of our Parasympathetic Nervous System (PNS) and what it does is to establish if a threat does exist and if not to relax the SNS response and rebalance.

➢ When in parasympathetic mode, our nervous system relaxes. We 'rest and digest', we heal.

CHAPTER 3

Why some people develop CFS and others do not despite similar levels of exposure to stress

I have drawn the conclusion that this illness can be linked to two underlying causes, the first being what emotional baggage we have inherited from our parents, the second resulting from the attachment style we developed in childhood, the general coping strategies we did or did not learn, and our innate response to any experience.

Epigenetics

The study of epigenetics may hold the answer to the hereditary aspect of our response to stress. Studies have found that genes are turned on or off depending on a person's experience, and that we actually may inherit unresolved shock/ trauma from generations past (Franklin 2010; Dias, 2014). Genes that have been turned on in previous generations are what lead to susceptibility and inherited weakness in our life. So, if we have already inherited a predisposition to fear and anxiety there is a high chance we can compound the problem based on our current life experience, our relationship to our primary caregiver, our home life in general and that of society around us.

Thinking about epigenetics I do not have to look too far back in my family tree to see the impact of stress and trauma. Both sides of my family where impacted by World War II, loss of loved ones, their homes and businesses. Taking this into consideration I can now look back at what I know about the experiences in my family history and see how it links to my experience of the world. In so doing I am able to take an active role in understanding and consciously working toward releasing any trauma.

Attachment Theory

On the whole, how we relate to the world is determined at a very early age by how our parents related to us and to the world. The three styles of relating that develop as a result of the parenting one receives were first described by psychologist John Bowlby in his Attachment Theory as being 'securely attached', 'insecurely avoidant', and 'insecurely ambivalent' (Holme, 1993).

Parents love their children and want the best for them, but life is not straightforward and situations can be tricky. We must remember there is no right or wrong, or some magic formula that creates the perfect outcome. Each situation is unique. This attachment theory is an observation of the outcomes of interaction between primary caregiver and child. It is in no way to be taken as criticism, or to find fault with one's parents or self.

A child that has been brought up in an environment where parents/caregivers have put a high value on their relationship with the child will tend to grow up securely attached. These parents/caregivers would have been attentive to their child's needs, interested in what they had to say, and very supportive in their day-to-day activities and life ambitions. A child brought up in an environment where they are not given the amount of attention they need will tend to relate to the world with an underlying feeling of insecurity. This may be due to either a divorce, loss of a parent/ caregiver and/ or a parent's physical or mental illness. Or, as in the case of foster and adoptive children, they may have gone through several carers and thus had no one on whom they could depend on a regular basis. These children will grow up being either insecurely avoidant, where they shun too much contact with others, or insecurely ambivalent whereby they feel deeply unsure about entering in to a relationship with another.

Stephen Tatkin, a clinical professor in family medicine, in his book entitled Wired for Love (2011) explains how neuroscientists have found physiological differences between children who receive plenty of positive attention from adults and those who do not. Those who do:

- tend to be well integrated, as the mammalian and reptilian parts of their brains are more evolved;
- tend to develop more neural networks;
- are less impulsive and, on the whole, better able to handle their emotions. They are much better at managing their frustrations than less-secure children;
- tend to have a well-developed right brain;
- are more resilient to the ups and downs of life, and are more capable in social situations;
- have dumb and smart vagi that are well balanced;
- have a hypothalamus that conducts normal operations and feedback communication with the pituitary and adrenal glands, so they have a healthier physiological response to stress or dealing with new situations.

Self-Control

Structure, support and clear boundaries appear to be key elements that help a child (or even an adult) to develop the skill to know how to act and react appropriately in a situation. Children need structure to learn what is appropriate and what is not. They also need structure and support from others in order to feel safe. Learning boundaries, interestingly, gives a child freedom to explore and discover who they are and how they fit within the structure that exists in their family or community at large. It is clear by observing children with severe emotional and behavioral outbursts how they are able to calm down and reevaluate their lives when they are put in an environment where they feel safe and with strong role models, support and structure. What children learn in a secure environment is a level of self-control, self-awareness and focus. Self-control and focus have been found more predictive of a balanced and successful future than a person's IQ, meaning that no matter how intelligent you are, you also need emotional intelligence in order to be able effectively to live your life in an emotionally balanced way.

We need to examine ourselves. We need to look at what we can learn from our parents and their lives, and if possible that of our grandparents, what experiences may have seriously affected them and how they managed them. It may give us some real clues as to how and why we respond to situations in the way we do. It may also help our parents and our relationship with them.

We also need to look back over our relationship(s) with our parents and/ or other primary caregivers and determine which one of the relating/ attachment styles best describes us. This will help us to determine what level of emotional intelligence we have – what level of awareness we have of our needs, our ability to communicate them and ask for help. It may be helpful to ask yourself the following: are you aware of your own needs, or do you tend to be focused on taking care of others? Do you find that you are over-generous and leap to the aid of others, even to the detriment of your own wellbeing?

Suffering from AF and CFS actually provides you with an opportunity to take a closer look at your overall lifestyle. Do you enjoy the job you are in, or do you feel trapped? What level of expectations – your own or of those around you – exist in your day-to-day experience both at work and at home? What level of stress is there in your life? Do you have well-defined daily downtime? What level of joy exists in your life? When was the last time you just kicked back, relaxed and let the world go by without giving it a second thought, or simply observed it without feeling you had to 'do something'?

The conclusion I have drawn is that those who develop CFS feel insecure with how they relate to the world and others, and, to compensate, make a great deal of effort (use of willpower) to do what is expected of them. Prolonged use of our willpower leads to what is known as Decision Fatigue (Baumeister, 2011). If our lifestyle, both at work and at home, is steeped in stress with little or no downtime, then this feeling of being overwhelmed and tired begins to have a direct effect on our physical health. When set a task, we are able to draw on our willpower to do what we need to do, following which we have an energy slump and a desire to relax our mind. Prolonged Decision Fatigue leads to feeling overwhelmed and tired on a regular basis. The fatigue then becomes pathological and chronic, beginning with AF and for some leading on to CFS; the effect is documented on every system of the body, though observed particularly on the nervous and immune systems (Wilson, 2001).

Women and CFS

It has been found that women are more likely than men to suffer from CFS, with a ratio of around 3:1 (Dowsett & Ramsay, 1990). Why is that? This is a question that really troubled me. I could not really make sense of it. I hypothesized that maybe it was due to women taking on a more active role in the workforce and continuing to have a full family life as well. Having children, being pregnant and working at the same time is certainly hard work. That was not a satisfactory answer in my mind, though, as many men work long hours and are either single parents or do a lot in the home as well. So I went in search of any clues as to why women might be more vulnerable to developing CFS.

I found that neuroscientists did a study using an MRI scan to see whether men and women react differently to stress (Nauert, 2007). The results were fascinating in my opinion and began to shed some light on my quest. The researchers found that there is a difference in the response. In men, the Neocortex is activated in response to stress, meaning that more blood is supplied to this part of the brain for them to react; for a woman, it is the Limbic System that is triggered. This has led me to wonder whether a woman's innate physiological reaction to stress slows down her ability to engage the Social Engagement System, more so than it does for men. A new study at the University of Pennsylvania shows how male and female brains are actually differently wired (Verma, 2013). In summary of their findings they propose that this could form the basis of understanding why certain disorders are predominantly male and others female.

It will be very interesting to observe the results of future research findings in this area. I am quite certain that at some point scientists will be able to clearly map out male/female anatomical differences in the brain and how that translates to how either might be more susceptible to particular diseases. Intriguing.

CHAPTER 4:

Esoteric Perspective

So much research has been done on CFS, with a number of hypotheses put forward, yet there have been no clear answers as to how this disease develops nor why. In the previous chapters, I put forward a tangible view of how and why this disease unfolds, yet it does not touch upon the esoteric (energetic) aspect of our being. From an esoteric perspective, it is believed that CFS is caused by a considerable imbalance in our subtle bodies, thus resulting in this multi-system disease.

Physical and subtle bodies

What we identify with as our self is actually made up of different levels of vibrating energy, referred to as our subtle bodies. Along with the physical body there are also four subtle bodies: the emotional, mental, etheric and causal (soul) body.

Most people, as well as modern science, tend to identify only with the physical body. To fully recover from CFS we need to look at all levels of our being. We need to examine how to change our lifestyle and attitudes, take supplements when required, and have much rest. Yet we also need to understand energy healing and how to incorporate it into our path of recovery, as it is able to help address the root cause, which is the imbalance(s) in our subtle bodies.

Quantum physicists and mind/body researchers are discovering that energy healing is of vital importance to our wellbeing, but this (unfortunately) has not as yet been translated into any form of practical application within the existing health system in the Western world. This truth, like all other momentous truths of the past (eg. 'world is round, not flat'), will take its time to filter through to our collective consciousness.

Interestingly, Martin Miles in his book Homeopathy and Human Evolution, quotes Plato (382BC) who stated that "the cure of the part should not be attempted without treatment of the whole. No attempt should be made to cure the body," he said, "without the soul. If the head and the body are to be healthy you must begin by curing the mind... for this is the great error of our day in the treatment of the human body, that physicians first separate the soul from the body."

Scientists now know that we are an energetic structure, as is everything else we can perceive. Under a strong electron microscope any solid object becomes a foggy haze. Mind-body science and research are now beginning to discover and uncover evidence of what esoteric writers and philosophers have been trying to share with us for centuries: all is not quite what it seems. This draws me to the saying, "don't judge a book by its cover"; there is so much to us that does not readily meet the eye.

In relation to CFS, health and our life in general it is important to take into account the role our subtle bodies play. The etheric body, for example, is a blueprint to the physical body we identify with. The connection between the etheric-physical body is vital; it is what animates us and gives us life. We die when we permanently disconnect with our etheric body.

In his wonderfully enlightening book The Science of Spirituality, Lee Bladon (2007) explains how our etheric body is that which breathes life into our physical body and is connected to it via the energy centres referred to as the chakras. There are said to be thousands of small energy centres within and around our physical body, forming an energy matrix. The etheric body is essentially part of the overall intelligence system (guided by our causal body – commonly known as the soul) that scientists are now desperately trying to understand. It is this intelligence that keeps everything working in harmony and which circulates energy (known as chi, ki or the vital force) around our physical and subtle bodies to keep us vitalized. There are seven main chakras in the body, as they are the seven main points where several energy pathways cross over one another. In Chinese medicine, where needles are used to stimulate these energy pathways, CFS is referred to as a spleen-and-kidney-deficiency illness. In China, yin and yang energy are viewed as the two opposite principles in nature and when they are out of balance illness will result. Yin represents the feminine, passive and negative nature of things whilst yang represents the masculine, active and positive side. Too much of one can weaken the other; too much yang, for example, can lead to yin deficiency as in the case of CFS. From the Chinese energy model the extent to which CFS will be experienced will be proportionate to the severity of yin deficiency. Yin organs include the heart, lungs, liver, kidneys and spleen. Interestingly, it is the spleen chakra that accumulates energy during the day and distributes it around the body when we are asleep. This energizing and distribution system does not function as it should in patients suffering from CFS. From this alternative perspective of CFS the level of 'malfunction' or imbalance of the spleen chakra will determine the severity to which a person will experience CFS symptoms.

According to esoteric writers, as outlined by Bladon, approximately 75% of all ill health and disease results from an imbalance in one of our subtle bodies. The majority of physical symptoms are as a result of that imbalance being transferred down to the physical level via the intermediary subtle bodies. For an imbalance to make itself known to us it needs to register as a number of signs and symptoms in our physical body so we become conscious of the problem and take steps to address it.

It is said that 50% of all imbalances can be attributed to the emotional body (eg. emotional shock or trauma, suppressed emotion due to fear or insecurity), 25% to the mental body (eg. stress and tension) and 25% to an imbalance in either the physical or etheric body (accidents, poor nutrition), causing a partial disconnection to occur between the two. Depending on the situation we experience a number of signs and symptoms that we tend to cluster under 'disease' or 'syndrome' names. These signs and symptoms are the physical-etheric body's way of communicating a disconnect of some sort and that help is needed to restore harmony and a sense of wellbeing (Bladon 2007).

What connects our physical and subtle bodies, what gives us life as we know it, is our nervous system. The nerve that acts as a bridge, relaying information back and forth, between our Central Nervous System and Autonomic Nervous System as well as our physical and subtle bodies is the vagus nerve (its branches connect to the seven chakras, the seven major energy centers of your body); this nerve begins in our medulla (base of our brain, top of the spinal column), and extends throughout our body and is often referred to as the 'wandering nerve'. Through a series of neurotransmitters and electrical impulses the vagal neural network acknowledges, interprets and responds to every internal and external experience we have. Neuroscientists have found artificial Vagus Nerve Stimulation (VNS) to successfully help with depression, sleep disorders and epilepsy. They use a surgically implanted device that acts like a pacemaker that sends out electrical impulses. Because the vagus nerve (VN) has so many functions and has an effect on so many different regions of the brain, researchers are now looking in to VNS to help with anxiety disorders, migraines, tinnitus, fibromyalgia, eating disorders, chronic heart failure, traumatic brain injury, memory, mood disorders and severe mental disease.

Stimulating our VN results in a relaxing of our nervous system allowing it to perform optimally (as described in Chapter 2). There are three ways our bodies naturally support the healthy function of our VN: laughter, crying and breathing. When we laugh – a real laugh not a polite one – we can feel the tingles inside as the VN releases. I imagine laughter for the VN is the equivalent of a really satisfying stretch after a long ride on the bus or a plane. In fact, when we laugh very hard it also produces tears, perhaps allowing for a deeper release of emotion or tension. When we have experienced a sudden shock or fright, for example, we may then either laugh or cry – some do both – and our body trembles as the nervous system and body release the effects of our ANS jumping into fight or flight mode (see Chapter 2). When the body trembles it is in the process of releasing any tension and trauma accumulated in the body. I have recently been recommended a book by David Berceli entitled *The Revolutionary Trauma Release Process*. The process outlined in the booked is called TRE, which stands for Tension and Trauma Releasing Exercises. It is supposed to be very effective in releasing unresolved shock and trauma held by the body. You may wish to look into this.

I find it quite sad that we are taught from a young age to suppress our urges to laugh or cry in public when it is actually therapeutic for us. In the United Kingdom in 1997, when Princess Diana died, people were coming together, expressing their sorrow and crying with no shame. I remember at the time hearing people say that expressing their grief for the loss of Diana also acted as a valve for releasing other feelings of sadness they had kept inside. Perhaps we all need to find a way in social circumstances to feel able to express an emotion without it becoming a big deal.

Using our breath to induce a state of calm, clarity and to maintain good mental and physical health is something yogis – those who practice meditation and spiritual exercises – have been suggesting for hundreds of years. In the next chapter I give you a simple breathing exercise that is very useful but I also recommend that you look into it further, as there are various breathing techniques that have been shown to help rebalance the system.

We are in a very powerful position to restore our own health back to an optimum state by exploring the simple tools and techniques that exist and implementing the ones that suit us. Also, energy medicine and spiritual healers are able to work on our physical and subtle bodies to help us restore this balance. In the next chapter, I will describe a three-tiered approach to help you bring back your health and inner wellbeing.

CHAPTER 5

Treatment: A Three-Tier Approach
– A time to Reboot

An integrated approach to healing is what is required to recover from AF and CFS and in some cases we do need medical (alternative and orthodox) intervention. I will explain the alternative below, but it is important to recognize that for some, anti-depressants, taken with care, may also be necessary on their journey. What we need to remember is that anti-depressants act as a 'pause' button on our system; they do not have a curative effect, but can give the system and the person time to adjust and gain some strength. A big part of everyone's recovery, though, is working out why we developed this illness. We need to closely examine our lives and discover what changes need to be made. There is no one cure that heals all, because each of us developed CFS for different reasons and are experiencing it at different levels of severity.

I will outline a treatment strategy as to how you can effectively help yourself and what help you need to receive from others (your partner, children, GP and energy healers). This strategy is also effective and can be implemented by AF sufferers. I will give a brief explanation on each aspect for you to gain a basic understanding. You may then go on to do further reading on any treatment or aspect of treatment that resonates with you. For example, I did much better when treated with Craniosacral therapy and homeopathy than I did on acupuncture, whereas others have seen miraculous results with acupuncture. As I said, there is no fixed formula. We each have to move forward at our own pace and find what works for us. Remember to always give yourself permission to rest and do things in your own time. As much as possible try and avoid putting yourself under pressure.

On the following pages you will find a three-tiered approach that for me has been essential to regaining full health. When taking tinctures and supplements, please always seek the advice of a professional if you feel you need more than the regular recommended dose.

Tier 1: Physical-Subtle bodies: alternative therapies

When thinking about how energy medicine (alternative therapy) operates, I find it best to imagine our energy as a flow of intricately woven streams that circulate as one interdependent system. Over time, like a stream of water, debris begins to build, causing an obstruction that has a domino effect on the whole system. We register consciously the effect of any obstruction, whether caused by bacteria, an emotional shock or a physical trauma, through a variety of physiological and emotional signs and symptoms. As time passes, our experiences create a cumulative effect on the system and we begin to incorporate into our lives any limitations and pains that result.

It is very important to note that our cells are small bundles of energy that hold memory of unresolved shock, trauma and disease. We do not often realize this, but if you begin to notice then you will discover your body has a rhythm to it, unique to you, a particular way it responds to various stimuli as a result of your past. In recent years documented cases have come to light whereby heart transplant recipients exhibit behaviours that are uncharacteristic for them but characteristic of the donor. They may, for example, crave foods they never previously liked or enjoy extreme sports that formerly held no interest for them or begin to exhibit anxieties they never before experienced. The answer to such phenomena can only lie in the existence of cell memory. From this type of example it seems clear that our general behaviour and unresolved trauma both reside at a cellular level and may be triggered by certain stimuli.

Alternative therapies are particularly helpful in observing where any energetic/ physiological blocks are and assisting the body in resolving them.

❖ Acupuncture – Acupuncture is a part of Traditional Chinese Medicine (TCM) that has been practiced for thousands of years. A TCM energy chart outlines the flow of energy (chi) through the body along a number of channels called meridians. Health, according to TCM, is when the chi flows uninterrupted and in harmony throughout the network of meridians. Disease results when, due to physical or emotional trauma or shock, the energy is blocked. An acupuncturist is trained to establish if and where any energy blockages exists by taking your pulses. The body not only has a heart pulse as we in the West are used to taking, but also the pulses of the subtle bodies and the interaction between them. Once having established our state of health through the pulses, the acupuncturist will then insert thin needles into the body at the points where meridians require stimulation and rebalancing. Some acupuncturists, like my own, will also use Chinese herbs to support the system in its healing in between treatments.

❖ Craniosacral therapy – I felt a slight shift in my health from my first Craniosacral treatments in June 2012. Unfortunately, I could not be sure at the time if it was the acupuncture or Craniosacral therapy that helped, and I could not afford both therapies, so I chose to continue with the acupuncture as I was too afraid to stop it – it had proven very helpful to me in the past. By September, though, I realized the acupuncture was not working and I began regular Craniosacral treatment from early October at home once a week up until I went away in May. My therapist, Susannah Burton, very kindly put together a few words to describe Craniosacral therapy from her perspective as a therapist: "Craniosacral therapy is an extremely gentle yet profound whole body therapy, using a light touch, that aims to assist the body's natural capacity for self-repair. Working on the principle that health is always present, the treatment is supportive and holistic, and allows physiological wisdom of the body to show the specific priorities for our own healing, and how best to resolve any patterns held within the system. Through following the pace that the body determines Craniosacral therapy works gently to build up health and vitality and to enable deep rest and recovery, and so is well suited for babies, children and the elderly, as well as adults and people in fragile or acutely painful conditions.

Craniosacral therapy developed from discoveries made by Dr William Sutherland, an American osteopath, over 100 years ago. He noticed intrinsic movements of the bones of the skull, and later research revealed rhythmic tidal motions in the fluid systems of the body. He considered these movements to be a direct expression of health. Since then Craniosacral therapy has grown from clinical experience which shows that health is something active, and not just an absence of disease.

During a treatment, once my client is lying or sitting comfortably, I will make light contact with my hands and begin to listen to the subtle rhythms and patterns within their energy, tissue and fluid fields. I have no intention in this listening, only holding the body as a whole with a wide awareness and allowing the system to settle. Often, after a few minutes, there is a palpable drop into a sense of deeper relaxation, a systemic settling. I often feel this shift as having more of a sense of the whole field of tissues and fluids, a sense of warmth, a deepening. The client may feel it as having arrived on the table, feeling calm or sleepy, a feeling of stillness and deep relaxation. At this point I am able to follow the priorities of the body and listen with my hands to what needs attention. I may feel this as the tissues and fluids orientating around a particular area, a welling up, a pulling, or as a calling for attention. I will then move to this area and through my hands gently encourage a state of balance, a deeper stillness in which this particular pattern has the greatest opportunity to resolve.

There is often a feeling of softening, a sense of the tissues beginning to breathe, or a feeling of more space and ease. It is not uncommon for emotions to arise as patterns of experience express themselves, and I will work gently with my clients to make sure they feel safe and comfortable with this. Once there has been a resolution of a particular pattern another area of the body may call for attention, and then another. I do not determine what will happen next; it is the wisdom of the body that is directing the session. As the patterns resolve there is often more of a sense of the whole body connection, the tissues and fluids moving in harmony with each other and a feeling of deep physiological rest. Many people notice some immediate relief from symptoms, muscle and joint pains may lessen, anxiety decrease, breathing and digestion may improve. After a few sessions clients often say that their sleep patterns have improved, as has their ability to rest more deeply, to deal with any stresses and strains in their daily lives, and that they feel an increased sense of wellbeing, often extending to many aspects of life, including their emotional health and interpersonal relationships.

Bodies love to be listened to, and if heard with a soft, neutral touch that allows them to be themselves without being directed, their story will unfold. By gently listening and orientating to the health in the system, rather than focusing on areas of discomfort or disease, the body is able to listen to itself, to remember its incredible ability to move towards balance and health."

❖ Homeopathy – As a homeopath, I have been very passionate about homeopathy for the last few years and feel that it played a very important role in my overall recovery. Homeopathy is a holistic system of healing that focuses on the individual and not the disease. Therefore, from a homeopathic perspective there is no specific remedy that will help everyone. Your homeopath will take your case to determine which remedy is best suited to help restore balance to your system. The remedy will be chosen to fit you and your needs as an individual as opposed to treating the common symptoms of CFS. For example, ten people with CFS will all have had different life experiences that have led them to develop this illness and thus require individual remedies to address their needs.

For myself, I needed to address long-standing, deep grief that had not been resolved: my parents' divorce when I was nine, the stress of the events that led up to it, and losing my grandmother at 11, who was my rock. I was a very shy child and had great difficulty in expressing my emotions and asking for help. The way I responded to this trauma was unique to me and others experiencing this may have responded differently. In the last few years, leading up to my collapse with CFS I again experienced high levels of stress and grief that I was unable to express or deal with. Therefore a pattern emerged, showing how I internalized my emotions with no outlet, and my homeopath was able to prescribe remedies based on my response to life experiences.

There are many paths that lead people to develop CFS and

therefore are as many remedies to help. A homeopath will look at your life, what stress and trauma you have experienced and how you have responded to it emotionally, mentally and physically.

❖ Reiki – At first, I thought Reiki and spiritual healing were one and the same thing. They are not, though both are a form of energy healing. Reiki was developed by Mikao Usui in the early 1900s. He devised this therapy as a form of self-healing and spiritual development. Initially he called it a 'Method to Achieve Personal Perfection', and it was rooted in Tendai Buddhism, which provided spiritual teachings, and Shintoism, which gave methods of working with and controlling energies. In the West, even in Japan nowadays, Reiki is considered a form of alternative therapy rather than a self-healing tool. Reiki (pronounced 'Ray-Key') is a form of energetic healing.

A Japanese word, 'Rei' means universal and 'ki' means life force or energy, which flows in and around every living thing. This energy, generally referred to as 'chi', 'qi' or 'vital force', works its way through our energy channels or meridians. It promotes healing on a physical, mental, emotional and spiritual level, restoring balance and bringing a sense of calm, clarity and wellbeing.

In Reiki, the practitioner gently lays their hands on the recipient in order to stimulate the Parasympathetic Nervous System (PNS). When we are asleep or in a deep state of relaxation or meditation our PNS is activated. When activated, the body enters a state of 'rest and digest'. It is at this time that the body is able to attend to any adjustments that need to take place in order to bring it back in to a state of balance.

When we are awake, as explained in Chapter 2, our Sympathetic Nervous System (SNS) is activated and is responsible for what is commonly referred to as our 'fight or flight' response. It is the SNS that is active when we feel under pressure (stressed) and remains in an active state for as long as we feel overwhelmed. If stress persists our state of health goes out of balance as our SNS is unable to stand down and allow the PNS to fully take over. For us to remain in the best state of health possible mentally, emotionally and physically the SNS and PNS need to work together.

A Reiki practitioner has been taught how to go in to a deep state of meditation, allowing energy to flow freely in and around themselves and the person they are in contact with. This is a very therapeutic experience that encourages the recipient's body naturally to activate the PNS to restore a state of balance and harmony.

Most people find they will drift off to sleep during a Reiki session. In essence, a session can be described as the ultimate rejuvenating power nap. The Reiki therapist acts as a conduit through which universal (healing) energy flows, and the physical and subtle bodies use this to restore health and harmony.

The amazing thing is you do not need a Reiki practitioner long term. Anyone can receive Reiki training, and it is very easy to learn. All it requires is practice and dedication. It is very beneficial, as it allows you to give yourself a daily energy 'top up' to help support your body in its healing process. I would suggest you consider doing the training yourself; it can be done over a live Reiki course or home study course. There is a link to the course I did after the bibliography section.

❖ Spiritual healing – Amanda McGregor, my Reiki practitioner, is also a spiritual healer. I could not put in to words what spiritual healing is or what spiritual healing does; from what I have read it seems to differ from healer to healer; they each have their own gift and method for working on the physical and subtle bodies. I received regular Reiki and spiritual healing from Amanda, and felt a shift in my energy with each session. The feedback she gave me on the visions she had were also very valuable. Her visions would usually be in relation to what my emotional body was trying to work on and release. By pointing me in the right direction, she enabled me to do a lot of thinking and positive meditation on the issues that came up so that by the next treatment it was either cleared or on its way out. As I have always felt a tremendous benefit after receiving treatment from Amanda I asked her if she would write a few words to share with us from her perspective what it is she does:

"By tuning in with my fingers to the energy centres of the soul, the chakras and meridians, I am able to go on a journey in seeing in vision and truth the 'issues' that continue to effect the person I am working with. Often childhood traumas, projections, power issues, or boundary issues with others come up as an 'insecure' energy; that means the person isn't settled in to the central position of their 'power'. When a person like Helen is burnt out, there is a need to emotionally process past and present for the future to start moving the person forward. Often these areas of concern overwhelm the energy centre so the person cannot refuel their life force. I am able to pull away the conscious energy frequencies attached to insecurities, fear and pain, quickly and effectively. I tune in using my fingers and run their energy by unblocking and removing any low vibration emotions, giving them back a connection with Source and reconnecting them to an infinite supply of energy.

I channel high-vibration energy to enable them the uplift needed to process their issues easily, as the lower vibrations transform with ease and joy with a strong energetic channel. Often inner-child soul rescue is needed to re-align and integrate the self, so they become stronger and more sure of themselves. The inner child tends to be trapped at different times in their growth due to overwhelming hurdles they may have experienced in growing up, or their younger 'self' is simply 'stuck' in a position of lack, through neglect. The problems vary; I find it important to give reassurance, advice, compassion and love to reconnect the inner child with the adult self, thereby enabling a reintegration. If a person hasn't received much love in their life, they are often programmed (N.L.P.) not to receive energetically, which eventually catches up with them when they burn out. Facilitating, teaching and programming a person to receive care, compassion and healing enables a stable and constructive path forward, so gradually the person is strong enough to take back day-to-day responsibilities and re-engage with the busy life that surrounds them, choosing a more sustainable way of energy management, diet and communication in lifestyle and relationships. I am able to do all these processes in trance, but they are quite intense energetically to the CFS/ME sufferer, so with sensitive people who are low in energy I tend to be very gentle in my approach, choosing to stay conscious and fully present with the sufferings and joys that present in the journey of healing.

Helen is a very conscious person. She is a joy to work with. She fought a hard battle but won through remaining present with her inner journey, allowing herself to receive energy and healing so she could fully grow and become; just as a caterpillar has a time cocooned before it becomes a butterfly."

I remember in one of her early visions Amanda said, "When you overcome this I see you much stronger than you were before." At the time I did not realize how long this was going to last or how emotionally and physically painful it was going to be. Her words would drift back to me in some of my hardest and darkest moments and give me hope not to give up and that one day I would be okay, that I just needed to get through one step at a time. Through this, I realized the power of hope and how it can lay the foundation for recovery against all odds.

Breathing technique: grounding yourself

Breathing properly in general helps to ground our body and increase a balanced energy flow. Most of us do not actually breathe properly;

for example, a lot of us hold our breath while we wait for an answer or when thinking intensely, thus unintentionally causing distress to the body. Learning to be aware of our breathing, not forcing it or hindering it, is of great benefit to our wellbeing physically and psychologically. Until you master this, using a breathing technique to ground yourself is helpful. Here is an easy one you can try:

- First sit or lie somewhere peaceful. Make yourself comfortable then;
- Inhale to the count of four;
- Exhale to the count of six;
- Hold your breath to the count of six;
- Repeat for as long as you feel necessary.

Tier 2: Mental-Emotional – CFS life coaching

I think of this tier as a form of life coaching, which you can do by yourself or you can recruit the assistance of your partner, a close friend and/or a health practitioner. Some may beg to differ, but surprisingly it doesn't take too much time to deal with the psychological issues underlying your condition when using a combination of the approaches outlined in this section. Behaviour becomes very much automated over the years. Think about when you first learned to drive: every little thing you did you were aware of, yet in time you could drive somewhere and be surprised not to remember most of the trip. Mental habits develop in similar ways and they form the basis of how we respond to situations and ultimately how we feel about them. If we look at self-defeating beliefs such as defensiveness, feelings of inferiority, guilt, feeling that you are victimized, or that you have to constantly prove yourself, they produce an enormous amount of pressure on the nervous system. Therefore, to help rebalance the vagal neural network it is important to deal with any external pressures or threats that exist in our lives, as well as the internal 'threats' that exist in the form of negative or self-defeating mental habits.

a) Lifestyle changes

Here you need to take stock of how you are living your life and what is in it. This is not as simple as it sounds; we tend to justify everything we do and can get very defensive even when we challenge ourselves as to why we do something. Yet, if you're reading this and are suffering from CFS it is time to strip back and take a naked, objective look at your life.

The best way to do this is to imagine your life as a painting or a collage. Make a list of all the elements that make up your life, then transfer these onto a canvas. Your canvas can simply be four sheets of A4 printing paper stuck together with sellotape: you don't need to be Picasso, simply make sure you include everything. This is an exercise for you, and there's no right or wrong aspect. It just is what it is, so don't judge what you are doing, but simply observe what unfolds.

Now it is all there, would you say there is harmony to your life? Do things flow nicely? Are you living a balanced life or is it skewed more toward work, chores or fulfilling expectations? Pull it apart and decide what needs to go, what needs to be changed and what needs to be added.

After this, take another 'canvas' and, based on your new list, draw how your life will look when you implement these changes. You may need to sketch this out a few times until such time as your representation strikes a note of satisfaction in your heart. You will know you have achieved this when you smile without realizing it, knowing that this is how you want to live your life. When that smile appears, place that poster somewhere you can see it. Energy follows thought, action follows intent: when I was very ill I realized that only if you tend to your inner garden, meaning your own hopes and dreams, can you watch the world around you bloom. Give yourself permission to let go of all external expectations and remember who you are, then bring that to the surface.

b) Stress management tools and techniques

The first tools outlined below focus on what I classify as 'internal psychological issues' that you need to uncover, accept, resolve and let go of. The Journey work and the writing and drawing with your non-dominant hand techniques deal with ways of managing your internal environment, discovering how and why we relate and respond to the things the way we do. By uncovering 'the why' we are able to deal with whatever comes up and thus let go whatever grip it has on us. The Emotional Freedom Technique (EFT) gives you a clever tool to help release an emotionally charged response as it occurs.

To manage 'external psychological issues', such as interacting with other people and any external environment you find yourself in, I recommend The HeartMath Solution. The techniques outlined in this book can be implemented whilst you are experiencing a situation, and the more you practice them the easier it gets to find your balance when you find yourself in tricky or difficult circumstances.

The Journey (Bays, 2012)

I was recommended and began reading The Journey in March 2012, but it wasn't until May 2012 that I thought to ask for some help using this approach. Sorena Gamanescu, a colleague of my partner and a Journey work practitioner, offered to help me. I found it to be a surprisingly simple and powerful method of getting to the bottom of mental/ emotional blocks by finding the root cause and releasing the trauma that had been held onto by the psyche. It is a fascinating tool, using guided visualization to tap into the subconscious, and can be used when alone or ideally with the help of a friend. If you have a lot to work on (as I did) I suggest one or two initial sessions with a Journey work practitioner to help you on your way. In her book, Ms Bays tells her story, outlines the process and how it can help release you from psychological shocks and traumas, whether very past or from the present.

Recovery of Your Inner Child (Capacchione, 1991)

This technique involves writing and drawing with your non-dominant hand, which is said to tap into the part of our brain where our inner child resides. It involves accessing the region of our brain that feels our emotions and is intuitive, playful and creative. By reconnecting with the wisdom of our inner child, it helps to resolve emotional conflict, build relationships and restore health and wellbeing. I have to admit when I was suggested this book by my Craniosacral therapist, I was more than a bit skeptical. At the time I found it very difficult to read for more than three minutes in one sitting, and I didn't know how I would manage to read and do the writing and drawing activities suggested. Yet, I had to trust in my therapist, and I would do anything I could to help myself recover from the awful state I was in, so my partner ordered the book. It took me a month to do Part 1, but I really felt I gained some valuable insight from my perseverance. It actually cheered me up.

Emotional Freedom Technique (EFT)

In November 2012 my Reiki therapist Amanda suggested I look into trying some EFT to help relieve some of the emotional stress and sadness I was experiencing. I had heard of this technique but had not had any first-hand experience of it. My partner printed out some information from the website of The Energy Therapy Centre in London, where they describe EFT as "often referred to as 'Psychological acupressure'. The technique works by releasing blockages within the energy system, which are the source of emotional intensity and discomfort... An EFT treatment involves the use of fingertips rather than needles to tap on the end points of energy meridians that are situated just beneath the surface of the skin. The treatment is non-invasive and works on the ethos of making change as simple and as pain-free as possible... As such, EFT is being accepted more and more in medical and psychiatric circles as well as in the range of psychotherapies and healing disciplines... It is used extensively on physical issues, including chronic illness, with often astounding results." (www.theenergytherapycentre.co.uk)

I highly recommend visiting their website, which is very informative. It gives you EFT tapping points with a diagram showing the location of the most used points during an EFT treatment, as well as clear instructions on how to do the whole process. I found it very easy to follow and ended up using it every day. Now that I'm feeling better I have had a struggle with a dependence on chocolate and crisps, and have found that tapping has helped to reduce the struggle.

The HeartMath Solution
(Childre & Martin, 2000)

As mentioned previously, you need to examine every aspect of life by looking at which people and circumstances drain and/or stress you. Write that list carefully, examine what changes need to be made, then make a plan of how you will change or completely rid yourself of each thing that is not as it should be. Your plan should be realistic and work within a time frame that suits you. The aim is to follow your heart.

That, of course, is always easier said than done, yet to help you on your way there is an ingenious method, devised by the HeartMath Institute, that can bring a balance between the heart and mind.

HeartMath is an effective system to show you how to follow your heart. It will provide the tools, techniques and exercises to help you access your heart intelligence. Applying the advice and techniques they recommend will help to make your life better by helping relieve you of a lot of unnecessary stress. By using the Freeze Frame five-step approach and other methods outlined in this book you are able to calm your mind and allow your 'heart intelligence' (wisdom and intuition) to guide you on your next step.

In their book, Doc Childre and Howard Martin reveal that over the last 30 years a huge amount of research has been conducted to understand the emotional as well as physical workings of our heart. As a result, a large body of information has been amassed and continues to surprise the scientific community as to the depth and breadth of the heart's influence on our whole being. Below are just some key points they outline regarding the findings of our heart's function.

"Heart intelligence is the source of emotional intelligence."

"The heart has its own independent nervous system – a complex system referred to as 'the brain in the heart'."

The heart's "signals affect the amygdala, thalamus and the cortex."

"Core heart feelings affect both branches of the Autonomic Nervous System. They reduce the activity of the Sympathetic Nervous System and increase the activity of the Parasympathetic Nervous System... This collaboration results in diminished friction and wear and tear on the nerves and internal organs."

Gaining perspective

Learn as much as you can about any situation before entering it in order to reduce any unknown factors and the stress they could potentially cause. Do the same when you are about to meet new people; wherever possible, learn as much about them before arriving at the meeting, whether it be social or for work. I think we all underestimate the value of information in reducing a stress response in any new situation, and the information gained will make us feel safe and thus diffuse, or drastically reduce, the intensity of our initial response (orienting reflex) when we enter that situation.

Suggested guidelines to live by

Mikao Usui gave his Reiki students five precepts to live by. These were:

Just for today

- do not anger;
- do not worry;
- be humble;
- be honest (in your dealings with others);
- be compassionate towards yourself and others.

Added to these, give yourself permission to:

- take your time to respond to what you are experiencing;
- turn off your mobile phone and leave it off when you are having fun;
- not answer your mobile each time it rings when it is on;
- take your time to do what needs to be done;
- take time out when you need it so as to process what is going on around you;
- be honest with those around you by explaining how you feel and what your needs are;

- take three deep breaths to ground yourself whenever you enter into a novel situation, or whenever you feel you are becoming overwhelmed by a situation you are in. Centre yourself and aim to be true to who you are in any given experience;
- say, "I am not sure, I will have to get back to you on that" if you are unsure of how you feel when asked for your opinion. Do not feel obliged or pressured to respond swiftly.

Tier 3: Physical

Hyperbaric Oxygen Therapy (HBOT)

In April 2013 I was introduced to Hyperbaric Oxygen Therapy by a relative who mentioned that a friend suffering from CFS had found it very helpful. I didn't know much about HBOT, nor had I yet a full understanding of what CFS is to make an informed choice as to whether or not to pursue it. Also, at the time I really didn't have the energy reserves to look into it or feel strong enough to start something new just before our big trip to Greece – I was really very apprehensive about the trip – so we didn't pursue it then. I forgot about it until I returned.

I have since read a wonderful book called The Oxygen Revolution by Dr. Paul Harch and Virginia McCullough (Harch & McCullough, 2010). In it they describe how HBOT, which involves the use of a decompression chamber, "is effective in the reparation of any neurological condition". They explain how "it stimulates DNA to produce growth and repair hormones and the protein receptors on cells that respond to these hormones". This is because cells go into a neutral (non-reactive) state when traumatized, and with repeated exposure to HBOT treatment they are able to reboot themselves and thus reactivate from a point of health. The authors also explain how "repetitive exposure to hyperbaric oxygen causes new blood vessels to grow, and it can metabolically energize the cells. As a result, we get permanent changes in brain function as new blood supply grows." They mention how they had two CFS patients who were housebound, who came for treatment and who then felt sufficiently better to go back to work.

For those of us suffering from CFS this treatment – helping our neurological system to reboot after shutting down – sounds pretty amazing. In order to maintain our recovery and not relapse, though, we would still need to work on all the areas of supporting ourselves; mentally, emotionally, and physiologically in relation to our lifestyle. HBOT may potentially be able to help us to recover a lot faster, but we must also make changes in our lives to the factors that were behind our development of CFS in the first place.

Food

AF and CFS sufferers tend to experience a blood-sugar imbalance, predominantly hypoglycemia. Our blood sugar spikes and then goes very low, causing a desire for sweetened foods, snacks and caffeine to keep us going. This simply turns into a vicious cycle that I, for one, found hard to break. Having broken it, though, I feel more energized and better in myself from having changed what I eat and when. The following tips are good as a general guideline that you can implement in your life from here on out. If you have children, it will also do them a world of good to eat nutritiously from an early age and not pick up our bad habits. My son is almost three, and has not had a piece of chocolate or a lollypop as yet. I lived on crisps and chocolate before I had him; now I just do not have them in the house as I still find it very difficult to resist. Below are some golden rules we have managed to incorporate as part of our regular family eating habits rather than just mine. You too may find them useful.

Golden rules:

- Always choose organic or free-range produce where possible. Also try and eat fruit and vegetables according to the season in which they naturally grow.
- Aim to have five small meals a day rather than three large ones. It really helps to keep your sugar levels on more of an even keel. Also, do not skip a meal (particularly breakfast). If you are on the go it is always a good idea to have a healthy snack or small meal along with you in your bag. This is something I have been doing for years, and it has proven very beneficial. My partner always teases me that I travel with too much food, yet whenever there is a delay in a plane departure, or we're stranded somewhere with no shopping access, the food I have is praised and gobbled up!
- Have lean protein with every meal (chicken, red meat, fresh nuts and seeds, fish, tofu). For some people red meat is tiring to digest, for others it is needed to help boost energy levels. Test it out for yourself to see whether meat is helpful or not to you.
- Eat whole grains – if nothing else, aim to have brown rice as often as possible and avoid white pasta.
- Plenty of fresh vegetables and green salad.
- Avoid fried foods or eating at fast-food restaurants.
- Those with CFS should try and avoid heat-inducing spices such as chilli and ginger, as they will fire up and tire out an already burnt-out system.
- Replace caffeinated and fizzy drinks with herbal teas and water.
- Cut out alcohol and cigarettes.

- Eliminate refined grains (white rice and flour) as much as possible.
- Avoid foods that contain preservatives, additives and chemicals. One of my pet hates is aspartame, a synthetic food sweetener that is reported to be worse for our health than refined sugar. Scientists and researchers have tried for years to keep this additive out of our food, as it has been found to be a neurotoxin.

If you are thinking, "Shoot me now!", believe me, I know exactly how you feel. If I wasn't upset before having to go all 'super healthy', this really put me in a bad mood. I felt so awful, though, that any choice was taken out of my hands. I gratefully concede now how important it is to be aware of the food, drink and supplementation we can take, without which our health can really slip away through our fingers. Below I outline some herbal tinctures and vitamin supplements that may help improve your energy and stamina by supporting your overall health and vitality.

Tinctures and food supplements

The aim with tinctures and supplements is to strengthen the nervous system, immune system, the circulatory system and all vital organ function. When taking tinctures and supplements you need to monitor closely how you feel. This is because depending on how severely affected you are by CFS your body will need you to take it slow in order not to over-stimulate itself, meaning that if you're feeling very weak you must start with the minimum dose and work your way up as you get stronger. Also, as you get closer to full health again you need to minimize or completely stop using the tinctures and supplements.

Tinctures

Avena sativa (nervous system support): eight drops in a little water three times daily. I felt an immediate difference when I began this one, and I have taken it daily since starting it in April 2012.

Hydrastis canadensis (potent antibacterial/ antiviral): four drops in a little water twice daily, taken up to seven days. Repeat monthly if needed.

Ceanothus (spleen support), berberis vulgaris (kidney support), carduus marianus (liver support): take eight drops in a little water in rotation (eg ceanothus Mon, berberis Tue, carduus Wed and so on in rotation).

Supplements

B complex by Neal's Yard remedies: This is a nervous system support you can take once daily after a meal. I started by taking a third of the contents of one capsule mixed in with some hummus and worked my way up to a full capsule daily over about three weeks. As I was very weak initially I did not want to push my system faster than it could go. It is always a good idea to build up what you do slowly and always listen to your body as well as the advice of your healthcare practitioner.

Floradix: An iron supplement (10ml am/pm) for as long as you require. It is made from vegetables and does not have any adverse affect on the stomach. I took it twice daily, but I suggest you start with once, then see how you feel with twice. As always, listen to your body.

Vitamin D3 (Nature's Answer): two drops daily in some juice or hummus. Vitamin D is essential to our system and has been found to be deficient in CFS sufferers. If you are not getting out of your home at all or are unable to sit in the sun then this supplement will be of great benefit to you.

Solgar-B12 1000: Take once daily after a meal, breakfast ideally. B12 helps to boost energy and is an antioxidant.

BioCare – Adreno Complex: This is a very good support, specifically designed to aid the adrenals. The recommended dose is two times daily; I took it three times daily for a while, following a pharmacist's consent, as I found it to be a great help and felt better for it.

Viridian-Pycnogenol: A fantastic antioxidant. Take two times daily around snack time (11am, 3pm).

Viridian Co-Q10 100: Take as directed. Once daily is usually ideal. Co-Q10 helps to boost our energy by supporting cell mitochondrial function.

BioCare Vitamin C powder: 1g every three or four hours. Reduce amount as you feel stronger. Vitamin C is essential when the body is experiencing any level of stress. It is not produced naturally by the body, and more often than not we don't get enough of it from our diet. At one point I was taking up to 8g of Vitamin C per day. Any surplus your body does not require will be secreted via your urine. If we have taken a lot more than we need we will experience diarrhoea, so if you do then reduce the amount by 500g until you find the right dosage for you.

Pace yourself

Always ask yourself, "Should I?" rather than "Can I?" do the following. You will be surprised how helpful it is in stopping you doing something that will be detrimental to you. Think of your energy as savings in a bank account; try and always spend less and save more until you are fully recovered. When approaching any task, break it into manageable chunks, and focus on one aspect at a time. This will help reduce any pressure or frustration and will allow the brain to rejuvenate neural pathways that may have been more or less dormant during the time of your illness; this will depend on the severity with which you experienced CFS. Our neural pathways are not rigid but fluid, increasing and decreasing according to what we use them for. In essence, as we recover we need to re-educate our brain on the tasks we want to be doing again.

Like playing a particular sport for example, if you try and go back to it after years it will take some time to get your mind and body back to the levels to which they responded before. You will not need to learn the sport from scratch as cell memory comes back in to play, but if the body and/or the brain have not been in full use for any extended period of time, then rehabilitation is required. So take it slowly and build yourself back up to where you were before you fell ill. On average, it takes six to eight months to return to full functioning once you have recovered from CFS. It is not possible to simply snap back into home and work life. It is a gradual process of reintegration.

Mudras: Yoga in Your Hands (Hirschi, 2000)

Doing any form of exercise while suffering from CFS is impossible until such time as we have moved into the recovery phase. It was suggested that I try to do Yoga or QiQong to strengthen my system. I found it impossible as I could not sit or stand for months. There is a point from which you will feel sensory processing is easier and you're able to do some exercise and build up your strength and stamina, but before that time you will be depleting a very short supply of energy. As previously mentioned, use your energy conservatively as you would money in a savings account. Hand mudras (symbolic gestures) are therefore a clever way of moving energy around the body and stimulating it without much movement. In her book, Gertrud Hirschi explains what each hand mudra is helpful for and uses clear illustrations on how to achieve the special finger and hand positions.

Fun plan

This may sound ridiculous but it's not. As you move into your final phase of recovery and into full health, make a list of all the things you love, and things you would like to do. Make a plan of how to incorporate these things into your life. HeartMath can once again help in focusing your attention in achieving this goal. Remember to always give yourself permission to both rest and have fun.

Conclusion

The aim of this three-tiered treatment is to release pressure on our system mentally, emotionally and physically. It's about being able to identify our needs and make sure they are met. It's also about identifying people and situations that cause us undue stress, by placing unnecessary pressure on us. Once identified, we must not push ourselves through it but put in place a strategy of change, changing how we relate to people by setting firm boundaries and expressing our needs, and by changing the circumstances of a situation or leaving it. CFS can be overcome and a relapse is not a necessary thing if you manage your life by finding a balance between its demands and nurturing your needs.

Once our Autonomic Nervous System is properly functioning

again, it is up to us to ensure we don't put unnecessary strain on it. There will of course be times in our lives when it is stressful, but that is normal and you will have the reserves to get through it. Our system is simply not built to withstand ongoing stress, particularly if it is self-inflicted, without a break, such as pushing yourself to do more work all the time with no proper food or rest periods. It is about finding a way to live harmoniously and thus not overwhelming the brain.

CHAPTER 6:

Karma and Health

'Karma' means action and re-action. Good and bad karma essentially describes whether an action was 'good', leading us toward universal understanding, acceptance and enlightenment, or 'bad', which bodes ill to the self and others as a result of ignorance. Karma is the universe's way of helping us to evolve and move toward enlightenment. Our every thought, spoken word and action is a cause and depending on its nature, good or bad, it will result in an effect. This effect may be felt immediately or may filter through at a later point in this life or the next. Karma and reincarnation go hand in hand. The best way to think of karma is like a bank account that you are trying to balance, where the credit (good karma) pays off the debit (bad karma). It takes many lifetimes to manage this balance as we have seen by the few numbers of people who manage to attain enlightenment. It is not an easy journey, as we all know, but it is a very fair one, though it may not often appear to be so. This brings me to one aspect of our being, health, but what I will say also holds true for finances, love and happiness.

Our health very much depends on our actions and habits in our present life, but it also depends on what karmic baggage we may be carrying in relation to health from previous incarnations. There is no telling what each of us may need to help us on our journey of learning and enlightenment. For example, through this experience I discovered that I had to learn to stop and really start listening to my body. I had to learn to put my needs first rather than those of others. Most importantly, I had to stop worrying about what others thought of me, expected of me or wanted from me. It took this horrendous experience for me to realize I have spent practically my entire life in a state of anxiety, trying to be the 'perfect' person I thought I had to be. Although outwardly I always appeared supremely confident, inside it was a totally different story. I felt lonely, unhappy and suffocated by all the things I felt I ought to be doing. Now I feel much better, not only physically, but mentally/emotionally as well. I do not feel obliged to do anything; I do not feel responsible for everything, nor the need to jump to the assistance of anyone who crosses my path with a problem. No. Now I take my time and feel very content to spend quality time with my family and close friends. Everything else has taken a step back from my awareness, and I have relaxed knowing that life just is what it is and I do not have to get involved with everything going on around me. I feel liberated from a self-imposed prison.

So, the next time you ask yourself, 'Why ME?' or 'Why did I get ill?', 'What purpose does any illness serve?', the simple answer is it serves to help you become consciously aware of your whole self and to see what you can do to help restore balance, harmony and purpose to your life.

Epilogue

My motivation and desire in writing this book is to bring hope: hope through understanding, hope through empowerment. It has been a labour of love and a journey of discovery. Through these pages I discovered that there can only be one truth – my truth. This holds true for all of us. We need to listen to our hearts and thus follow our truth and inner wisdom.

We all cling to beliefs to give some structure to our world. We learn a variety of behaviours and expectations through our community and family. We are social creatures, yet we are also spiritual beings. Learn to let go of what you do not need and feel free to move with the flow of life.

Change is the only constant, so try to enjoy the ride by learning to let go of the past, embracing the present and looking forward to the future.

I wish you well on your journey.

Helen Germanos
East Sussex, July 2014

Acknowledgements

I would like to thank Morag and Michael for being by my side throughout this journey – in particular Morag for always being there no matter what, and Michael, for whom my love, I discovered, could conquer all. My parents, John and Grethe, for their unwavering love and support. To my friends Maria Lydaki and Stavros Volkos whose support gives me strength. To Amanda McGregor and Susannah Burton who were always there when I needed them. I would also like to thank Clementine Murray-Coronis, Fabiano Culora, Vicky Fikaris, Marina Koufidaki, Mark Griffin, Lambros Chudley and Bryony Weaver for their encouragement and support in helping me to cross the finish line and complete this book.

A collective thank you to all the CFS/ME sufferers, carers, researchers and neuroscientists from around the world for all the information they have discovered and shared that helped me in the process of understanding and putting my theory together.

Thank you to all the authors and publishers for their support and permission to reprint the information found in this book.

'Hope' is the thing with feathers[11]

By Emily Dickinson

'Hope' is the thing with feathers –
That perches in the soul –
And sings the tune without the words –
And never stops – at all –
And sweetest – in the Gale – is heard –
And sore must be the storm –
That could abash the little Bird
That kept so many warm –
I've heard it in the chillest land –
And on the strangest Sea –
Yet – never – in Extremity,
It asked a crumb – of me.

Reference/ Bibliography

Baumeister, R.F. and Tierney, J., 2011. Willpower: Why Self-Control is the Secret to Success. London: Penguin Group.

Bays, B., 2012. The Journey: A Practical Guide to Healing Your Life and Setting Yourself Free, 2nd ed. UK, London: HarperElement.

Bladon, L., 2007. The Science of Spirituality. UK: EsotericScience.org

Brooks, D., 2012. The Social Animal: The Hidden Sources of Love, Character, and Achievement. London: Random House.

Capacchione, L., 1991. Recovery of Your Inner Child. New York, NY: Simon & Schuster.

Childre, D., and Martin, H., 2000. The HeartMath Solution. New York, NY: HarperCollins Publishers.

Chopra, D., 2009. Reinventing The Body, Resurrecting The Soul. London: Ebury Publishing.

Elias, J., and Ketcham, K., 1998. Chinese Medicine for Maximum Immunity. New York, NY: Three Rivers Press.

Farhi, D., 1996. The Breathing Book. New York, NY: Henry Holt & Co, LLC.

Goldstein, J., 1996. Betrayal by the Brain. New York, NY: Routledge.

Griffith, C., 2011. The New Materia Medica: Volume 2. London: Watkins Publishing.

Harch, P., and McCullough, V., 2010. The Oxygen Revolution. USA: Hatherleigh Press.

"Henry David Thoreau." 12 May 2014, Xplore Inc.

BrainyQuote.com. Available at: http://www.brainyquote.com /quotes/quotes/h/henrydavid122202.html

Hirschi, G., 2000. Mudras: Yoga in Your Hands. Newburyport, MA: Red Wheel/Weiser.

Holmes, J., 1993. John Bowlby & Attachment Theory. London: Routledge.

LeDoux, J., 1998. The Emotional Brain. London: Phoenix/ Orion Books Ltd.

Marieb, E., 2006. Essentials of Human Anatomy & Physiology, 8th ed. Pearson Education Inc. San Fransisco, USA.

Miles, M., 1992. Homeopathy and Human Evolution. Kent, UK: Winter Press.

Myhill, S., 2014. Diagnosing and Treating Chronic Fatigue Syndrome (CFS), 29th ed. London: Hammersmith Health Books.

Porges, S.W. Orienting in a defensive world: Mammalian modifications of our evolutionary heritage. A Poyvagal Theory. Psychophysiology 1995;32:301–18.

Porges, S.W., 2011. The Polyvagal Theory. New York, NY: W.W. Norton & Company Inc.

Sapolsky, R., 2004. Why Zebras Don't Get Ulcers. New York, NY: St Martin's Press.

Shapiro, D., 1990. The BodyMind Workbook. Dorset, UK: Element Books Limited.

Smits, T., 2011. Inspiring Homeopathy: Treatment of Universal Layers. Haarlem, The Netherlands: Emryss Publishers.

Tatkin, S., 2012. Wired for Love. Oakland, CA: New Harbinger Publications Inc..

Verrillo, E., 2012. Chronic Fatigue Syndrome: A Treatment Guide, 2nd ed. (Kindle edition).

Wilson, J., 2002. Adrenal Fatigue: The 21st Century Stress Syndrome. Petaluma, CA: Smart Publications.

Online article and studies

Barill, T & Dare, Michael. 2007. Managing Cardiac Emergencies. 2nd edn. Vancouver, Canada: SkillStat Press.

Connor, S., 2013. The hardwired differences between male and female brains could explain why men are 'better at map reading'. The Independent, 3 December. Available at: www.independent.co.uk

De Lange, FP., Kalkman, JS., Bleijenberg, G., et al. Gray matter volume reduction in the Chronic Fatigue Syndrome. Neuroimage 2005; 26(3):777–81.

Dias, BG., Ressler, KJ. Parental Olfactory Experience Influences Behaviour and Neural Structure in Subsequent Generations. Nature Neuroscience 17 (2014), pages 89–96.

Dowsett, EG, et al. Myalgic Encephalomyelitis – a persistent enteroviral infection? Post Graduate Medical Journal 66 (1990), pages 526–530.

Franklin, TB., Russig, H., Weiss, IC., et al. Epigenetic transmission of the impact of early stress across generations. Biol Psychiatry, 2010; 68 (5): 408–415.

ME Society of America. Left Ventricular Function in Chronic Fatigue Syndrome (CFS): Data from Nuclear Ventriculography Studies of Response to exercise and postural. Available at: www.cfids-cab.org/MESA/cardiac.html

Myhill, S., 2009. CFS is Heart Failure Secondary to Mitochondrial Malfunction. Available at: www.cfids-cab.org/MESA/DrMyhill-373.pdf

Nauert, R., 2007 Response to Stress is Gender Specific. Available at: http://psychcentral.com/news/2007/11/20/response-to-stress-is-gender-specific/1559.html

Peckerman, A., LaManca, JJ., Dahl, KA., et al. Abnormal impedence cardiograph predicts symptom severity in Chronic Fatigue

Syndrome. AM J Med Sci 2003; 362(2):55–66.

Porges, SW. Orienting in a defensive world: Mammalian modifications of our evolutionary heritage. A Polyvagal Theory. Psychophysiology, 32(1995), 301–318. Cambridge University Press, USA.

Puri, BK., Jakeman, PM., Agour, M. et al. Regional grey and white matter volumetric changes in Myalgic Encephalomyelitis (chronic fatigue syndrome): a voxel-based morphometry 3-T MRI study. Br J Radiol. 2012;85(1015):e270–3.

Tanaka, M., Sadato, N., Okada, T., et al. Reduced responsiveness is an essential feature of chronic fatigue syndrome: a fMRI study. BMC Neurol. 2006 Feb 22; 6:9.

NHS diagnosis criteria for CFS:

www.nhs.uk/Conditions/Chronic-fatigue-syndrome/Pages/Diagnosis.aspx

Canadian diagnosis criteria for CFS:

www.cfids-cab.org/MESA/ccpc.html

Therapists

Craniosacral therapist, Susannah Burton.
www.susannahburton.com

Journey work practitioner and Homeopath, Sorina Gamanescu.
sorinagamanescu@gmail.com

Homeopath and Reiki practitioner, Helen Germanos.
www.helengermanos.com